The large black bicycle, which I stand beside in the hallway, still looks as impressive as it had yesterday; in fact it looks even mightier now I am to deal with it alone. Mrs O' Reilly and I had done a practice run of loading the bike, but now the large wooden box and its cylinders seem not to want to be strapped on to the stand which lies over the back wheel, and the black delivery bag, containing all the tools I will need to do the job, seems to be too big to be wedged into a basket which lies over the front wheel. Having made noise enough to waken the dead, never mind the Stones who live on the ground floor, I am off. I negotiate through the front door and bump down the front steps, the door stays open behind me and the light stays on; Mrs. O'Reilly appears to have gone back to bed. I attempt to lean the bike against a fence which lies on my right, but with its load of paraphernalia the bike starts to slide down as soon as I let go of it. Catching the handle bars before they hit the ground I pull the bike upright, and feel more than hear my stocking rip.

Dot May Dunn was born in Derbyshire, the daughter of a miner. In 1951 she joined the newly established National Health Service as a pre-nursing student at Leicester Royal Infirmary, eventually becoming a Research Fellow at St Bartholomew's London and the London Hospital Medical College. She has four nursing qualifications and 50 years on the 'coal face' behind her. She divides her time between England and France.

Twelve Babies on a Bike

Diary of a Pupil Midwife

DOT MAY DUNN

Although the events and the characters in this book are based on real experiences, all names have been changed.

An Orion paperback

First published in Great Britain in 2009
by Quay Books Division, MA Healthcare Ltd
This paperback edition published in 2010
by Orion Books Ltd,
Orion House, 5 Upper St Martin's Lane,
London WC2H 9EA

An Hachette UK company

Typeset at The Spartan Press Ltd,
Lymington, Hants

Printed and bound in Great Britain by
CPI Group (UK) Ltd, Croydon, CRO 4YY

The Orion Publishing Group's policy is to use papers that
are natural, renewable and recyclable products and
made from wood grown in sustainable forests. The logging
and manufacturing processes are expected to conform to
the environmental regulations of the country of origin.

www.orionbooks.co.uk

To Ellen O'Brien, who taught me midwifery and humility

Prologue

The year is 1956, and in the war-torn slums of a Midland city a young midwife is completing her professional training. Under the guidance of a strict but experienced supervisor, twelve babies must be delivered. To this end she has to go out alone into the dark and often inhospitable streets.

Carrying all essentials with her on her trusty old black bicycle, she encounters seedy slums, city brothels, Hitler's bomb sites, post-war council estates, and the genteel hanging on by their fingertips. With fortitude, the babies are successfully brought into the world.

Her diaries tell her story.

1

Monday 19th March

3.30 a.m.

A bell is ringing and I am pedalling fast, in fact I am pedalling so fast that I am gasping for breath, but still the bell rings behind me. The ringing changes; now it is the bell on a police car, loud and almost upon me. A bright light flashes across my brain, and a voice thunders above me.

'You've got to learn to answer the phone when it rings at night you know.'

I am sitting upright in a small, low-slung bed. The electric light, in its Bakelite shade, illuminates the lower part of the white wall that faces me, and with absolute accuracy and reverent precision, the shade manages to keep the icon of the Catholic Church in shadow. The voice calls out again.

'Well come on then, answer it, or it will be the chap on the other end of the line who will need your help, never mind his wife.'

I am out of bed, and as my feet land on cold linoleum consciousness hits me. This is to be the first delivery I attend alone; this is to be me, on my own, as a midwife. Mrs O'Reilly and I have carried out several home deliveries together, and she has declared me safe to try a solo run. Yesterday we visited all pending cases and discussed them at length and last night it was decided that I should attend the next case alone.

The figure at the door has gone, and the phone is ringing persistently, it is filling the small dark landing outside my door with its urgent call. I look from left to right; I had not paid attention to such detail on previous days. The low-intensity light snaps on and the space around me comes into view. I murmur, 'Thank you.'

The black telephone, which hangs on the wall just off to my right, is almost jumping out of its stand. My feet are bare, my pyjama legs drag on the linoleum, and my heart bangs loudly as I step over and lift the earpiece. I don't need to place the phone to my ear, I can hear the voice shouting 'nurse' as I hold the black Bakelite earpiece at arm's length. The word nurse brings me to my senses, and I know that I must gain control of the situation, so, with my lips to the mouth piece on the wall and the earpiece of the phone to my ear, I start the process.

'Hello! Mrs O'Reilly's house, Pupil Midwife Compton speaking, may I help you?'

The voice at the other end of the line is loud, in fact it is so loud that I can hardly understand it, and for a moment I wonder if I would hear the man better if I just listened out for him out of my bedroom window.

'Is that the nurse? Tell her to come, my wife has started. Hello! Hello! Are you there, nurse?'

In a quiet voice and with all the professionalism I can muster at this hour in the morning, I reply, 'Yes, I am here, now could you please tell me who you are?'

In an even louder voice he shouts, 'It's not me as wants you, nurse, it's the missus.'

For a moment I am lost.

'Yes, so what is your wife's name?'

Without a moment's hesitation he shouts, 'Clara, nurse.'

I shake my head to check if I am still asleep, and then ask, 'Is that her surname?'

'No, nurse, that's the same as mine is.'

Good, we're getting somewhere.

'Which is what?' I enquire.

'Oh! Right it's . . .' Brrrrrrrrrrrr.

The long continuous sound of a dead line assaults my ear, and as I press the empty cradle of the phone up and down it is now my turn to shout.

'Hello! Hello! Put some more money in please.'

But nothing happens, and I stare at the now dead earpiece.

The light clicks on in the clinical room, and bright light floods the first floor landing below. Falling over my pyjama legs I drop down the single flight of stairs, calling out as I go.

'He rang off before I got his name. Will he ring back? Do you think that he will ring back?'

Mrs O'Reilly stands impassive, the light reflecting on her glasses makes it difficult for me to see her eyes, but I don't need to see them, the straight, hard mouth says it all. Now, as she pulls her maroon dressing gown around her, the words come.

'No I don't think he will ring back, the money he used to ring once was probably all he had on him. Do you think men around here have spare shillings in their pockets, Nurse Compton? Well, I will tell you they don't, and that is why you must answer the phone when it rings and not when you feel ready to get out of your bed to answer it. Did you get anything from him?'

Now I feel ready for tears, the confident, assured Registered Nurse, with six months midwifery under her belt, feels humble and at a loss, as I mumble, 'He said her name was Clara.'

She looks at me over her glasses, and for a moment the eyes soften.

'Then you'd better get into uniform before Mrs Burns gives birth without your help.'

The blue dress, with its high white collar, hangs on its hanger behind the bedroom door, and the round pillbox hat and navy blue mac hang ready for action. I fight my way into the dress with more haste than speed, and with my SRN badge pinned firmly at the neck of the dress and a good-sized ladder creeping down my left stocking, I fall back down the stairs.

Mrs O'Reilly stands in the clinical room, a set of notes in her hand, and beckons me over.

'We don't know a lot about Mrs Burns, she was with Mrs Quinn until last week, but as Mrs Quinn is expecting her fourth at any time we won't get much help from that midwife.'

I cross the small room, with its many white cupboards, small electric sterilizer, clean white tables and locked drug cupboard. It is crowded, but in this room I am at home and, with the smell of antiseptic around me, I feel more confident. I pick up the large black delivery bag, which I had packed with such care yesterday afternoon and, trying to sound professional, I ask, 'Is there anything particular that I should look out for?'

Mrs O'Reilly continues to peruse the notes. We have both already read these several times, and I start to feel a little annoyed that she should doubt my ability to understand the issues raised in them, after all I had taken third place in my Hospital Part One Midwifery Examinations and had obtained a merit in Clinical Examination. She cuts through my angry thoughts, as, with a hesitant voice, which is still directed at the papers in her hands, she mumbles, 'It's just that I have only seen her once.'

As if seeking some hidden information, or code, she turns the pages of the notes, and speaks to them again.

'It's her third, shouldn't be a great problem, the other two labours were fine.'

Eager to get going, and ready to prove my ability, I ask, 'Do we know where she lives?'

Pushing the notes at me she lifts a large brown wooden box. This box, which I had checked twice yesterday, contains the gas and air machine. Two small cylinders lie side by side, one with black and white markings contains air, the other with red and white markings contains nitrous oxide which is commonly known as laughing gas. I find this name ironic as most of the women to whom I have given the gas were doing anything but laughing. However, when a fellow pupil and I had tried it out in the labour wards at the hospital where we had completed our First Part Midwifery Course, the effect obtained had been better than a couple of gin and tonics. Mrs O'Reilly's voice is crisp as she brings me back to the job in hand.

'I know where she lives, and so do you, you visited her yesterday afternoon.'

As I take the gas and air machine I sink, the box is heavy on my shoulder, but, as I look at Mrs O'Reilly's face, the realisation of the enormity of the task that lies before me weighs even heavier. My journeys around the district with Mrs O'Reilly had been, to say the least, confusing. In much of the patch there seemed to be few landmarks or distinguishing points from which to navigate. Each street seemed to look exactly like every other one with long rows of houses, most of them three stories high, opening onto pavements or very small front gardens, and as we had turned corners and gone on our way I had soon felt lost. Mrs O'Reilly's area has undergone some development; new flats and council houses have been built in the few years since the end of the War. A small piece of land, which is proclaimed to be a park and playground, lies within its bounds, and from what I had seen on my evening journeys, this park offers several types of sport, some of which could soon be causing Mrs O'Reilly an increased workload. Mrs Quinn's district, part of which we had just inherited, lies on the city centre side of Mrs O'Reilly's district. It holds no charms that I can distinguish, and like uncharted waters it appears to be unnavigable. On our first ride around Mrs Quinn's area Mrs O'Reilly had informed me that the morals of the place left a good deal to be desired. A girl who is on the midwifery course with me told me that her midwife says that it is the city's 'red light' area.

The voice beside me is speaking.

'She lives at number 36, Turnbull Street, Flat 2. That's just inside Mrs Quinn's district so it's not too far for you to ride.'

3.50 a.m.

The large black bicycle, which I stand beside in the hallway, still looks as impressive as it had yesterday; in fact it looks even mightier now I am to deal with it alone. Mrs O'Reilly and I had done a practice run of loading the bike, but now the large wooden box and its cylinders seem not to want to be strapped onto the stand which lies over the back wheel, and the black delivery bag, containing all the tools I will need to do the job, seems to be too big to be wedged into a basket which lies over the front wheel. Having made noise enough to waken the dead, never mind the Stones who live on the ground floor, I am off. I negotiate my way through the front door and bump down the front steps. The door stays open behind me and the light stays on. Mrs O'Reilly appears to have gone back to bed. I attempt to lean the bike against a fence which lies on my right, but with its load the bike starts to fall over as soon as I let go of it. Catching the handlebars before they hit the ground I pull the bike upright, and feel more of my stocking rip. With the bike now suitably placed I climb the two steps and close the front door. For a moment I had thought about slamming the door, but Mrs O'Reilly's face flashes before my eyes, and I close it quietly. There had been light on the path when the door was open, but now, as Mrs O'Reilly clicks off her bedroom light, I am in complete darkness. Claiming the bike, I head to where I know the gate lies, and banging open what remains of the construction I make for what I hope is the pavement edge. A gust of icy wind whips my legs and rain hits me in the face. For a moment I can't breath, and all my clothes, which I now realise are rather lightweight, blow wildly around me. The light from the bicycle lamp helps in the confusion; it lights up whirling flakes of snow and drops of rain, which are reflected back to me in a glitter. I stand and try to adjust my body to the cold and the dark.

There is hardly room for me on the bike, but I press my foot down on the pedal, and with a tremendous sway move from the pavement edge. With wobbly wheel and unsteady balance I move forward; the lamp goes out and I am heading to where I have no idea. Leaning over the delivery bag I give the lamp, or at least what I hope is the lamp, a thump with my gloved hand and a light shines again. I know that I must turn to my right at a small cross-roads, which lies just two houses up the road from Mrs O'Reilly's house. But am I now peddling up the wrong side of the road, or have I somehow got onto the wrong road? My light finds the corner, and I sigh sooner than I can say 'Thank goodness', as I turn and set off in what I hope is the right direction.

After a few pushes on the pedals I start to gather speed. Good, I can manage the weight. I know my midwife's home lies a little higher than the city centre house to which I am heading, but I had not realised how much higher. Snowflakes whirl towards me; they are the only things that my feeble light illuminates. A beam of light from a window shows bright against the darkness, and for a moment I see a hedge in front of a house. The hedge passes, I am travelling quickly. I apply the brakes, nothing happens. I gather speed, the wheels swish as water spins out from them and, fighting to keep the bike upright, I whirl onwards into the next swirling cloud of light. For a moment I am in darkness, my lamp has gone out, so I lean over and hit it again. As I look up I see bright lights ahead.

The only road to have light at this hour in the morning is the main road into the city, and I realise that I am heading at some speed towards it. I know that I must cross this road in order to get to Mrs Quinn's area, but in my mind I had planned to approach it with more caution. Now I have no idea how I will stop when I get to it, or in which direction I will turn if I can't stop. But I have little time to worry about such issues, as the bike makes all the decisions. As it leaves the dark steep road, I am just a passenger; its weight propels it forward, and we both whirl headlong into the light. I gasp for breath and let go of my hat; it takes both hands to pull the bike around. Now I am riding on the white line down the centre of the road. Something dark appears on my left side and I start wobbling again, is it a car? I hear a voice, and risk a sideways glance. A policeman on a bicycle is riding at my side; a large gloved hand is raised towards me, and I can see more than hear that he is shouting at me. The road is now flatter, so, with a good deal more wobbling, the application of brakes and the pressure of my shoe sole on the road, I bring my vehicle to a standstill. With the sudden stop I find that I am unable to hold the weight of my load; I and my bike fall sideways. I had inadvertently moved over to my left and had been travelling very close to the policeman. I catch him by surprise, and in a confusion of bikes, legs and uniform hats, we both land on the pavement.

3.57 a.m.

The young man adjusts the strap of his helmet under his chin as he reclaims his bike, and I press my pillbox back on my head.

'I didn't recognise you there nurse, you came at me so fast, almost took me with you, better be careful on these roads, lucky there is no one around at this time in the morning. You got an urgent case to go to?'

I am now able to breathe again and, as I pull my dress down to cover my knee, which is now sticking out through my stocking, and attempt to regain control of the brown box, which is continuing on towards town, I gasp my apology, 'Sorry, I couldn't stop.'

He looks down at me; he must be over six feet tall while I just made the five feet necessary for entering nursing. Taking a notebook from his top pocket he looks at his wrist-watch, and makes an entrance in the book. I blush, am I now to be arrested for knocking a policeman over?

'Where are you going, nurse?' He asks this without looking at me.

Now I remember Mrs Burns, and I reply as I struggle to get back on my bike.

'I am going to 36 Turnbull Street, I think that is the name of the street, I'm afraid I must hurry, her husband called some time ago.'

Putting the notebook back in his top pocket he swings his leg over his bike and starts moving beside me.

'You new around here, nurse?

Without waiting for an answer, he continues, 'Bit of a

rough area this is you know, do you want me to ride along with you?'

'Do you know where the street is?'

I had almost forgotten about the problem of finding the house; surviving the journey had taken all my attention. But now a knight on a black steed has come, and maybe he knows the way. He replies from his straight upright position as he throws his cape over his shoulder.

'I think that we might find it, nurse.'

4.05 a.m.

I see him standing in the doorway as we turn the corner into one of the grey, narrow streets. A morning gas lamp sheds its yellow glow on the front of the all-purpose corner shop, but no name adorns any wall, the street is nameless. The voice beside me speaks.

'This is the street, nurse, and by the look of him the anxious father is waiting for you.'

At the sound of voices the man moves forward, but on closer inspection of who is arriving he retreats back into the house. The policeman's voice sounds loud as he calls to the man who now stands in the open doorway.

'Mr Burns is it? Come on, sir, help the nurse with her equipment.'

I drop my feet and climb off the bike. A man in a collarless blue-grey linen shirt with an unshaven face takes hold of its handlebars. The now familiar voice speaks beside me.

'Goodbye, nurse, good luck.'

I watch the policeman disappear into the still-dark morning. His lamp throws light on the road as he passes and curtains in windows drop back into place. With the ease of one accustomed to such tasks, Mr Burns lifts the brown box and, without a word to me, heads up a flight of bare stairs. Wheeling my bike through the door, I follow him. An elderly lady stands on the small first-floor landing. She is dressed in grey worn clothes and she wrings the apron she is wearing around her thin, lined hands. Mr Burns calls out as he climbs.

'It's the nurse, Mrs Megs. I think that we will be all right now.'

Pale eyes look down at me from a face that matches the clothes.

'God bless you, nurse. God bless you for coming. Shall I stay in case you need me?'

I am at a bit of a loss to know what to say, I don't know who she is. Maybe Mr Burns should decide, but the woman looks as though she has some experience of life, so I give it a second thought and decide that I had better hold on to her.

'If Mr Burns wants you to stay that will be fine by me, Mrs Megs.'

In the light of the first floor landing Mr Burns looks at me for the first time. I am as yet only twenty two years of age, my stature is small, and last week when I was going back to the hospital in my uniform the conductor of a crowded bus had told me to stand up and let an adult take my seat. Now Mr Burns looks from me and back to Mrs Megs.

'Yes, you can stop, Maud, if it will help the nurse.'

The room is of a fair size. It is sparsely furnished, clean, and it holds the marks of a home well cared for. To my left a dressing-table with a cracked mirror stands before a window, its once dark brown surface has lost some of its veneer. Pale finger-marks stretch inwards from its edges, showing light against the polished veneer. Small brightly coloured doilies do their best to hide the faults. The lower half of flower-patterned curtains disappear behind the cracked mirror, and a small box with a cover to match the curtains stands before the dressing table. The far wall is dominated by a dark oak coloured wardrobe which, like its partner the dressing-table, has a few missing sections of veneer. Holding my bag before me, I enter the room. I had been here yesterday with Mrs O'Reilly so I know that a large double bed lies behind the door and takes up much of the remaining space in the room. The furniture, I know, will be arranged as requested for the confinement.

I had not heard Mrs Burns as I climb the stairs, and wonder if she has yet taken to her bed, but now, as I round the door, I see her lying on the bed. Drawing her knees up to meet her greatly distended abdomen she reaches for the upright poles on the back of the bed and, pulling hard on them, she starts to shout out. I drop the bag and hasten to her side as I call out to her, 'All right, Mrs Burns, breathe in and out, big breaths, in through your nose and out through your mouth, come on big puffs, blow hard.'

With one hand I feel her abdomen, it is hard and she looks at me through round pain-filled eyes. Sweat stands out over her face and neck, and I call out over my shoulder, 'Mrs Megs, get me a cold flannel, quickly.'

I hear shuffling, something damp is pushed into my hand, and as I put the cloth to Mrs Burns' brow I recognise it as a piece of someone's old cotton vest. The contraction recedes and Mrs Burns starts to relax. Now she looks at me and offers a weak smile. I give her the piece of cotton vest and she wipes her face.

'Thank God you're here, nurse, this is a bad one, I can't remember the two boys being this bad.'

She is, according to her notes, a woman of thirty years, but now she looks a good deal older; with her brown hair stuck to her forehead and her pale face lined with exhaustion, she could be forty. She turns to her husband and holds out the piece of vest.

'George, can't you find a proper face cloth for the nurse and not this old rag?'

George steps towards her with a bemused look on his face, but before he can do anything about the cloth his wife shouts out and, grabbing for the back of the bed again, she pulls her buttocks off the bed. I call out as I throw my coat over a chair which stands beside the wardrobe, 'Mr Burns, put the gas and air machine on the bed; put it near to your wife so that she can use it.'

He looks at me with startled eyes, and I shout as I wave my hand towards the box which stands upright near the bottom of the bed.

'The brown box, will you put it on the bed and open it up, please?'

Opening my bag, which stands on the floor, I take out the foetal stethoscope, but there is no time to listen to the baby's heart, the contraction is at its height. I head around the bed. Mr Burns stands by the open box and looks down at his wife. The smell of the gas rises as I twist open the valve on top of the cylinder, and the gauge, which denotes a flow of gas, springs into action. Leaning over the woman, who is now arched like tensile steel, I push the mask over her face.

'Breathe in and out, Mrs Burns, take some big breaths, as big as you can.'

She grasps the mask and, as I push her finger over the hole at its base, she gulps at the gas. Like a drowning woman gasping for air she pulls and the machine makes its familiar rattling sound as gas is drawn through the valve. Mr Burns has started to retreat at my approach, but, grasping his sleeve, I halt him and pull him over.

'Sit there by your wife, Mr Burns, and every time she has a contraction you give her the mask and help her to keep her finger over the hole. When the contraction ends she can move her finger so that she will just breathe fresh air.'

For a moment he looks from the cylinders to the mask and back, and then he nods his head and sits. Now he has something to do, something he understands, a piece of machinery that makes a familiar noise, he can go to work. Mrs Burns' voice breaks out from behind the mask.

'I want to push, nurse, I must push.'

I am beside her with hand on her abdomen, I speak close to her face and my voice is urgent.

'Not yet, Mrs Burns, breathe hard on the gas, don't push yet. Mr Burns, help your wife breath through the mask.'

Over my shoulder I shout to Mrs Megs.

'Can I have a kettle of boiling water, quickly please?'

She may not look much, but she knows her stuff, and I am very relieved when, almost before I have finished asking, the large black kettle is carried into the room. I hear water being poured into the large basin I have placed on the floor by the chair, and a small table, which I have covered with newspaper, now holds my delivery bag. I cannot say that things are now automatic, it is, after all, the first time that I have worked so totally alone. However I now start to sense that I am on known territory, and with a feeling of confidence I wash my hands, open the delivery bag, and put on my white delivery gown. Mrs Burns' contractions are now arriving with great rapidity, and I make the assumption that the baby is due to be born, but I know that I must check that all is well before I can safely ask Mrs Burns to do her job and push her baby out.

When the next contraction recedes, I tell Mrs Burns that I am going to examine her to see if the baby is due to come.

'It won't take a minute, and then we will know if you can start to push.'

I don clean surgical gloves, apply the right amount of lubricant, and with my surgical mask covering my lower face, I turn towards my now silent audience and start the examination. I fully expect to feel the round, firm top of the baby's head waiting inside the cervix, but now I stand in bemused disbelief, what presents itself is not what I had expected. The round, smooth top of a head is not there, at my fingers lies a soft mass whose outline I cannot discern. Is this a baby at all? Mrs O'Reilly had been right that we knew little about this pregnancy, and since I arrived I have had no time to make an external examination. Now my fingers make out something hard and, as I traced it along, I dare hardly let my mind accept what I think I am feeling. Scarcely daring to breathe, I feel again for the singular, pointed edge, and following it down I find the curved arches. My mind whirls through all the clinical teaching; it can be but one thing. I withdraw my gloved hand, and cold disbelief hits me, the baby is trying to be born with its forehead first. I swish my hands in the now cooling water in the basin, and my mind feels blank as I stare at the damaged wooden surface of the wardrobe. But I must think, I must make my mind work. Placing my wet gloved fingertips together, I turn and walk towards the door, and then, turning, I walk back to the wardrobe. Water drips from my hands, and I pull the gloves off with a sharp snap. The baby will not be able to make it, even though all is ready for it to be born. In this position it cannot get through the birth canal. The man's eyes meet mine as he rises to standing. Pulling my mask down I speak in what I think is a calm voice although a wobble sounds.

'Mr Burns, go and phone the midwife, and tell her to get here as quickly as she can.'

Bemused, he continues to stand by his wife and look at me. Now I shout, the stress of the moment forcing urgency into my voice.

'Run, man, run as fast as you can. Tell her it's a brow.'

He is up and heading down the stairs, his feet banging on the wooden steps; a child's cry sounds as his steps recede. Giving me a weak smile, Mrs Megs leaves the room, and I hear her feet ascending the wooden stairs.

'Is everything all right nurse? Has something gone wrong? Is the baby dead?' Mrs Burns asks.

Mrs Burns is rising up in the bed and, as if to climb out and take care of her yet unborn child, she struggles to get up.

'Everything is all right, Mrs Burns, I just want you not to push yet.'

She continues in her effort to rise, but the next contraction throws her back to the bed. I lean over her and push the mask over her face as I almost shout, 'Don't push, don't push, some big breaths, Mrs Burns, come on, big breaths.'

I know that I have to slow things down until the midwife arrives. My mind races through lectures as I help Mrs Burns hold the face mask. Seeking for inspiration, I try to recall lecturers' voices and lecture notes, why had I not been more attentive? Pethidine is the only answer I can come up with, but this might affect the baby's chances of breathing after it is born. My mind races and, as I pace the small room again, I know if I don't do something the baby won't get a chance to be born, and its mother may die. I call to Mrs Burns as I draw the fluid into the syringe.

'I'm just going to give you an injection, Mrs Burns, it will make you relax a little.'

The injection is in. I hear feet thumping on the stairs. Mr Burns enters, his face is flushed and still. He throws his arms out sideways and, expanding his lung enough to allow him to he speak, he gasps, 'I couldn't phone, I haven't got any money.'

The truth of Mrs O'Reilly's words hits me; he had used all his money for the phone call which got me out of bed. The next contraction is here, for a moment Mrs Burns gulps at the gas and air, and then she almost shouts, 'I've got to push nurse.'

With a cry she falls back on the bed and pushes. I must stop the pushing or the baby will be damaged, and Mrs Burns will soon become exhausted. Frantically I sift through a sea of knowledge which I have gathered throughout my years of training and which, until this moment, had seemed to be almost superfluous. I had worked for some months on a medical ward which was run by an older sister. Some of the younger sisters had said that she was getting a bit past it; 'time to retire' they had said behind her back, but I had liked her style of nursing and I was pleased that she did not retire before my time on that ward had expired. Now her face swims before me, and I hear her voice.

'Raise the foot of the bed if you want to take pressure off the abdominal organs. Help defy gravity,' she used to say.

Would defying gravity help here? We could try, the pethidine has taken the edge off things, but the contractions are still strong. So, more with hope than any professional expectation, I call out, 'Mr Burns, I want you to lift the foot of the bed, please.'

He is standing in the doorway, his face no longer red, is now a deathly white. Without question or hesitancy he walks past me and he lifts the bottom of the heavy wooden bed two feet off the ground. Mrs Burns slides backwards, and as I remove several pillows she arrives close to the head of the bed. A contraction comes and goes, Mrs Burns' urgency to push has lessened, maybe the pethidine,

I think. A child cries somewhere above us and then is quiet. Mr Burns does not flicker, he holds the bed.

I looked at him as, with less than steady hands, I pull the top of clean gloves over the sleeves of my now not so clean, gown.

'You can put the bed end on that box, Mr Burns, if you want.'

He half smiles, tension showing in his still white face.

'You do what you've got to do nurse, I'll hold the bed.'

I now feel calmer, I don't know what I expect to find when I do the examination, but I do know if things are unchanged the next step is a sprint to the phone box and a 999 call.

There is less pressure on the soft mass, it is not bulging as it had been, and I again seek for the pointed edge, the point which will tell me that I am feeling the forehead. I do not find it, now the arched ridges of the eyes are there, and as I trace them along they begin to feel more central and prominent. For a moment I am unsure, and then, like the first cords of the 'Halleluiah chorus' ringing out, the truth hits me. My mentor smiles at me and as I mentally thank her for her careful teaching. I almost shout, 'Push, Mrs Burns, push now, push as hard as you can.'

With the pressure taken off the last contraction had caused the baby to tip his or her head backwards, just a little lift of the chin, but that little has done the job, and now our protagonist is going to appear nose first, we can make it.

4.55 a.m.

The slit eyes and the red swollen face lie before me. The little pink body begins to move, I lift her, and the cry comes. I call out, 'It's a girl; you've got a girl, Mrs Burns.'

The voice behind me shouts, 'We've done it, Cla, we've gone and done it.'

Mr Burns is still holding the bed. Everything had happened fast, and I had forgotten the bed and Mr Burns, but now I could hug him.

'You can put the bed down, it's all over now, we've made it.'

Without a word he drops the bed-end, it lands with a resounding thump, and although his face is white the smile is large and real.

Wrapped in a surgical towel, the baby lies in her mother's arms.

'Isn't she beautiful, George? Just think, we've got a girl at last, won't the boys be excited.'

Mr Burns stands some feet away from the bed, and looks across at his wife and daughter. He looks at me, and I can see the glint of tears. With my mask pulled down, I smile at him.

'You can sit by your wife, and hold your daughter if you'd like to, Mr Burns.'

Quickly he moves his eyes from mine, steps over to the bedside, kisses his wife's forehead and looks at the baby's swollen face.

'Better not hold her, a big lump like me, might hurt her.'

His wife smiles up at him, and then looks back at the baby. I know I have some explaining to do.

'I'm afraid she got a bit squashed on the way out, she didn't come head first as she should have, she decided to lead with her chin.'

Mr Burns bursts out laughing, as if letting out all his tension. His wife looks at him in amazement.

'What's the matter, George, you gone mad?'

'I was just wondering who she looks like with that

round face and slit eyes, it's your mother she takes after, and if she led with her chin, it's certainly your mother.'

For a minute Mrs Burns is not sure whether she should take this declaration as praise or insult. But the moment is happy so, after further examination of her daughter, Mrs Burns replies, 'Yes, she does look rather like my mother; she will be pleased when I tell her she's got a granddaughter who looks like her.'

'Have you decided what you will call her? Maybe she can have her grandma's name,' I say as I start to clear up and put the delivery bag back together. It is Mr Burns who replies.

'Can't have her name, it's Maud. What's your name nurse?'

I look over my shoulder at them. Mr Burns still stands by the bed, he looks pale, but his eyes sparkle as he smiles. Intent on completing the notes before I forget the times of events, I reply without much thought.

'Oh! It's Dorothy Elizabeth.'

Now I feel quite embarrassed, and I can feel myself blushing as I rearrange the face mask that is hanging down my front. They both look back at the baby, who I am pleased to say has now started to move her head around a little, and Mrs Burns speaks, 'I like Elizabeth; maybe we can name her Elizabeth Maud.'

Before anything else can be said the door opens with a creak, and two small figures peer tentatively around its side. They are followed by the face of Mrs Megs. When he sees his mother the smaller boy bounds over, and throws himself onto the bed.

'Mind your baby sister,' his father shouts in mock chastisement, and Mrs Megs calls out.

'Oh, you got a girl, I told you as how girls was always awkward, told you it had to be a girl.'

'A cup of tea for the good lady I think, Mrs Megs.'

She smiles an almost toothless smile at me as she looks up from the baby.

'Kettle's boiling as we speak, nurse.'

As she passes me, I speak only for her hearing, 'Thank you for your help, Mrs Megs, couldn't have managed without you.'

She touches my arm in its white delivery gown, and then shakes her fingers as if to apologise for touching me. I take the grey-clad arm and squeeze it.

6.05 a.m.

Tea and biscuits are served to all present, and Mrs Burns leans back against her now clean pillows. The boys are back in their room and I take time to attend to the baby. Mr Burns stands behind me; I had not heard his approach.

'Touch and go there for a minute, eh nurse?'

I not sure how to answer, so I am silent.

'Nearly buggered it up, didn't I? Not having the right money like.'

How could I tell him that it was I who had wasted his money?

'Mr Burns, you did all you could, in fact you did more than enough, holding the bed . . .'

I get no further, a loud bang sounds on the front door, and a minute later I hear Mrs O'Reilly's voice as Mr Burns escorts her up the stairs.

She looks down at the baby's face as it lies placid on my lap.

'It was a face presentation; she was fully when I got here, so I couldn't do much.'

Now I realise how tired I am and what great risks I had taken. I feel exhausted, both physically and mentally. What if the baby is damaged, what if she is blind, what if I have given the pethidine too late?

'When I arrived it was a brow presentation and she was pushing, I gave her pethidine to slow things down.'

My voice fades; she looks at the baby and touches its face, the baby turns towards the finger and the swollen lips purse.

'Awake enough to feed, she is, I'll get the doctor to pop in and look at her, should be all right, not the first face delivery, and it won't be the last.'

8.15 a.m.

My legs feel like jelly. How I will ride home I'm not sure. Mr Burns has loaded the bike, and now daylight awakens the dull, grey street, and the sight of the dirty gutter and the wet, slimy pavement does little to raise my flagging spirit. I set off. At least I now have one point of reference in this mass of grey; a picture of the Burns house will remain lodged in my memory for ever.

2

Wednesday 21st March

7.30 a.m.

'It looks to me as though we are going to have some more snow before this winter ends.'

In Derbyshire it often snows in March, so the slate grey sky which shows through the skylight window is no surprise to me. In fact the snows often lasted well into April during the war years when I was a child. But now, as my father would say, I am soft-centred since I lived in the south of England for several years. However now I am back in the Midlands and snow at this time of year is seen as the rule, not the exception.

Mrs O'Reilly sits eating toast and sipping tea. The room feels warm and I am conscious of a burning sensation on the top of my head. As I look up I realise that a single-bar electric fire, which is attached to the wall over my head, has been switched on. I rub my hand across the top of my head, but Mrs O'Reilly makes no comment, and continues reading her newspaper. Without looking up from her paper she slides a cellophane packet over towards me; it contains a pair of stockings. When I had retuned to the house yesterday, Mrs O'Reilly had not been in. A loaf of bread, a bottle of milk, and a teapot had stood on the table in the kitchen along with a note in Mrs O'Reilly's hand.

'Make yourself some breakfast. Have gone to do the

clinic, don't come down, go and have a rest. These stockings are for you.'

I had lifted the cellophane packet; black material showed through the paper, and the words *forty denier black stockings* were written on the front of the package. Even in my state of exhaustion I had recoiled with revulsion, forty denier stockings? I had never owned such things, never mind worn them. Fifteen denier, yes, maybe even twenty for work, but who wore forty denier?

I feel her eyes on me as she looks at me over the top of her paper.

'I saw Mrs Burns' doctor yesterday. He has seen the baby and says that she looks fine. But you had better go in to see her first thing, might take some coaxing to get that baby to feed.'

She hesitates for a moment but her eyes continue to watch me.

'Better wear those stockings before you freeze to death, and I've put a blue scarf out for you, it looks and feels like snow.'

Without further comment she rises and leaves.

Yesterday evening we had written up the details of the delivery in the large official delivery book, and we had recorded in the drug book the amount of pethidine that I had used. I had signed for it and Mrs O'Reilly had countersigned. The times, examinations and findings were entered with clinical accuracy; no other comment was made. With the same care and accuracy I had entered the same findings in my Pupil Midwife's Case Book. But as I read it to myself it holds none of the stress and drama, and Mr Burns' part in the events goes unmentioned. Nothing has been said, but as I look at the stockings and think about the scarf I feel they might be an intimation that I am accepted, and am now trusted to go out alone on my black steed. I realise that I depend on, and must uphold, Mrs O'Reilly's good reputation if I am to get twelve deliveries successfully recorded in my Case Book.

1.55 p.m.

The class gathers, there are twenty of us in this February to July set. We know each other well as we have spent some time working together in the maternity department of this large teaching hospital, but now we are scattered around the city, each living with a district midwife. We are to return to the parent hospital on this and every Wednesday afternoon; firstly, to report to our respective tutor who is ultimately responsible for our progress; secondly, to continue with lectures mainly on community administrations; and thirdly, and for us, most importantly, to keep up with the social chat among friends.

'I've got three cases, how are you doing, Dot?'

Maureen speaks. She is my best friend, at least that is what I call her, and it is what other people call her. But I am never too sure about Maureen's intentions towards me. We have known each other since our student nurse days and have always competed for prime position in the exams. I couldn't really remember taking part in these competitions, and was usually quite pleased when Maureen did well. If I did well she would effervesce all over me, but other friends would tell me how she had belittled my success. I had once been accused of cheating; someone had said that they had seen me with a book in the exam room. My name had been cleared, but, as the saying goes, if you throw mud some of it will stick, and my results had dropped a good deal, and for some time Maureen had sought other friends. We had completed our nurse training on the same date, and with several other girls we had started our Part One Midwifery training at a hospital in a London suburb. Her name is Crawford, mine is Compton, so on most alphabetically organised events we are placed together, and in our Part One training we had found ourselves billeted together. Our friendship, or whatever you might call it, had begun again. Maureen had obtained a distinction for her Part One Midwifery written exam and a credit in Clinical Midwifery. I had a credit in the written exam and a credit in the clinical part, well down in the rankings. This had not overly concerned me, Maureen could enjoy the accolades. What had concerned me, however, and still did concern me, was her behaviour towards me concerning a boyfriend. We had spent time with medical students in the hospital in London; they were doing their midwifery and obstetrics clinical course in the hospital where we were working. I had become friendly with one of the young men, and we had been to the theatre together. He was a very polite and well-mannered young man, and I had very much enjoyed my evening out. Some days later, when we were in the common room where we all had to wait for the theatre midwives to announce an imminent delivery, a midwifery student who I did not know said, 'You're doing all right with young Jimmy, aren't you?'

When I feigned a lack of understanding, she continued, 'Come on, don't tell me you don't know that he's the catch of the year, you must know his dad is loaded.'

Maureen, who was sitting in the corner facing me, had looked at me over her book, but had said nothing.

Later the young man had called for me at our lodgings. I was still dressing and, on the pretext of finding a book, Maureen had left the room. A few days later we were again gathered in the common room. Jimmy was sitting next to me and Maureen was studiously ignoring everyone. Jimmy reached over and pulled a piece of my hair. It was then the fashion to dye parts of your hair different colours, and I had dyed the front of mine blond in order that I would be able to spray it with different colours.

'I can't resist a blonde, always fancy blondes,' Jimmy had laughed as he pulled my hair. Maureen's laugh was different; as it rang out from the corner of the room, it held derision and mockery.

'She's not a blonde, it's straight from the bottle, I should know, I help her to do it, and if you want to know what else is false about her, just you ask me. Know all your skeletons, don't I, Dot?'

The bell had rung and we had been off, a delivery will wait for no one. A couple of weeks later the medical students left and I never spoke to or saw Jimmy again. One of the girls had said that Maureen and Jimmy had had a good chat.

After the exams, several of the group of Part One Midwifery students had applied to this Midlands hospital. It is a newly built teaching hospital and places are much sought after. Both Maureen and I had applied and been accepted. Now once again she has hooked her arm through mine and has announced our friendship to all.

'So, how many have you delivered, Dot?' Maureen's voice rings out across the room. I ignore the question.

'Don't tell me you haven't got any yet, I would have thought the pros in the brothels around your area would have been dropping them like flies.'

My mind flashed to Mrs Burns; her clean home, beautiful children and devoted husband, all need defending, but the lecturer's entrance at that moment silences us.

4.30 p.m.

The lectures are over, our tutors have been visited, and I have done a good deal of explaining about my one and only delivery. We leave the School of Midwifery and head towards the main road and the buses. Some students head into town to catch their buses and I see the back of Maureen's head bobbing along in this group. She stops and turns, her face is now wet with a mixture of rain and snow, and I more see her words than hear them.

'Are you going to "the hop" this Saturday?'

I reply almost without thinking, and as the words blow across on the wind I know that I should not have released them.

'No, I'm going out with Tony.'

The lips speak again.

'You still going out with him?'

I hold my hand around my ear pretending that I can't hear. Our bus arrives, it throws sheets of cold water upwards as it slows down, and we run backwards across the pavement, shouting as we go. The bus stops well beyond the bus-stop, and with hands holding onto hats, and bags flying behind us, we run after it. The conductor hangs off the step of the bus, his hand hovering over the bell. We make it and, leaping over the gutter full of iced water, we clamber onto the step of the bus.

'Crikey, what's this, the birth of a nation?'

The bus conductor, a short, thin, middle-aged man, laughs loudly at his own joke. Adjusting his cap so that it sits on the back of his head he pushes the last of us up the stairs, and we head skyward for a quick fag.

5.30 p.m.

It is dark when I arrive back at the midwife's house, and as I open the front door Mrs Stone hurries down the passage towards me, switching on the light as she comes. She is a woman about a couple of inches taller than me, and on first sight appears to be quite plump, but, on better acquaintance, you realise that it is her very round face that gives the appearance of plumpness, she is in fact quite slim. The mother of two teenaged children, whose behaviour is so exemplary that I have hardly been aware of their presence in the house, she works constantly. The three of them, and sometimes when Mr Stone is at home from his construction work, four of them, live in the ground floor flat; that is, the flat below Mrs O'Reilly's. Mrs Stone acts as Mrs O'Reilly's housekeeper. She cleans and sometimes cooks for her, and she also minds the phone when Mrs O'Reilly is out. She is, I know, Mrs O'Reilly's right-hand woman, and is well trusted. I will soon realised that she is a woman to cultivate. Welcome hot drinks and biscuits can, when she feels inclined, be produced at the most inconvenient hours. Now she pushes past me without speaking, and then, turning behind me, she presses me forward.

'Mrs O'Reilly is waiting for you, had me looking out for you for the last half hour.'

Turning slightly to acknowledge receipt of her message, I set off up the stairs. The light is on in the clinical room. I hear movement, and start to take off my outdoor coat before I enter its clean white environment. Mrs O'Reilly is wearing her grey outdoor coat and her grey round hat with its midwife's badge pinned to the front. For a moment she ignores me as she gathers up the black bag, and pushes the brown box across the floor with her foot. Now she looks up and, without acknowledging me, she speaks.

'Don't take your coat off, Mrs Wardle's mother rang half an hour ago I've got everything ready. Those tutors dragging you in and out of hospital, they'll have you missing half of your deliveries. You'd think they were the only ones who know anything about delivering a baby. Hmm, I doubt if some of them can remember how to do it.'

Pushing the bag towards me she turns and, retrieving the notes which lie open on the table, she passes them over to me. I take them and, without glancing at them, I push them into the front of the delivery bag. Her eyes follow the notes and she opens her mouth as if to speak, closes it again, sighs, and then says, 'You've seen her a couple of times haven't you? Second baby, I can't foresee any problems.'

I am anxious to get going, my second delivery is imminent. I was the only one in the class who didn't have two deliveries. I haven't time for niceties such as reading the notes. I have read them several times already, what more can I see? So, tightening my coat belt and pushing down my hat, I seize the bag, lean over towards the gas and air machine, and reply, 'Yes, I examined her yesterday, everything was normal.'

Mrs O'Reilly's hand takes mine before it reaches the box, and I feel something hard press against my palm. I look down at my hand and back to her face, a shilling lies in my palm.

'For the phone call, should you need reassurance.'

Now my face is red and hot and, as I tumble down the stairs, she follows me. Mrs Stone stands at the bottom of the stairs, a cup of tea in one hand and a couple of biscuits in the other.

'Here you are, nurse, you might need these before you set off.'

I am about to say that I don't have time, the urgency of my mission is too great, but Mrs O'Reilly says, 'Better have them, you don't know when you might get anything else. Don't want Mrs Wardle using your shilling to ring and say that the midwife has collapsed. I'll have a cup, Joan, if the pot's still warm.'

Gulping some of the hot tea, I push both the biscuits

into my mouth and, as the two women retreat into the warm, well-lit kitchen, I head for my trusty black steed.

6.10 p.m.

All my journeys seem to start with a downhill ride, but now I am able to manipulate this over-large bike better since Mrs O'Reilly's neighbour kindly lowered the seat for me. The downhill ride and the main road have become less of an adventure as I have been to see Mrs Burns several times, and so I have gained some experience. Baby Elizabeth is doing fine, I am pleased to say. She has even started to feed and, apart from receiving what I think will be one of many whacks across her person from her brothers, she's doing well. The wind is blowing and the rain has turned back to snow, the hill is steep and, with the gas and air machine behind me, I do battle to stay at the side of the road. But this time I know where I'm going, and now I turn into the side entrance of one of the large houses whose fronts line the main road into town.

This is my third visit to this once grand Georgian house, whose gates once admitted horse-drawn carriages and whose steps have been scrubbed by maids, but which now stands dark and uncared for. I know that trees grow out from its cellar; I have seen the long, thin branches which lie against the side and back walls of the house. I drop my feet onto what remains of the once wide gravel drive and, alighting, wheel my bicycle across to what was once a small flower garden. I lean it against a bay window whose one and only curtain hangs askew across a dimly lit window. A flight of stone steps lies before me. I am just considering how best I might mount them, for on my previous visits I had been told by several people to take my bike with me into the house, when a young man appears in the large open doorway at the top of the steps. The light at the front of the house is patchy, it comes from one of the street lamps on the main road and it is filtered through a tall ill-kept hedge before it offers the house illumination. The tall thin man stands for a moment, pulls his large cap down around his ears, and tightens the overlong scarf around his neck. Then, as a figure joins him from the dark house, he turns, and as the light catches his face I see that he is a man of West Indian origin. With the tall, thin woman clinging onto his arm he descends the steps at speed, and almost knocks my bike over. Swinging himself and the young lady sideways he turns and shouts, 'What you parked there for, man? What a stupid place to park your bike, you could have killed me, man.'

His face is now close to mine as he bends forwards, and I see the dark brown eyes frowning beneath the large peak of his cap. The young lady – well I'm not sure if she is young now that I get a better look at her, or even a lady – smiles at me over his shoulder as he continues to shout into my face.

'You mad, you from some sort of nut-house or something?'

During this onslaught I am trying hard to stop the bike from falling over. The woman pulls at his arm, and he part turns to her as she speaks in a low voice and continues to smile at me.

'Errol be quiet, it's the nurse, and she's probably trying to get to see someone.'

Now Errol turns and looks me up and down.

'You a nurse? Oh! I'm very sorry, nurse, I didn't recognise you there.'

He swings himself sideways, pushing the woman away from me, and then, with his mouth stretched into a broad smile, he says, 'But if you got any spare time tonight, I'll be very ill if you will come and look after me.'

He falls towards me as if in a faint, and I smile as I reply,

'I'm a midwife, and if you will help me to get my bike up the steps I will be pleased to deliver your baby for you.'

At this his female companion roars with laughter, and the smoke-induced coarseness soon dissolves itself into a fit of coughing which sounds as though it needs medical help. After scowling at me for a few moments, Errol walks around the bike and starts to lift it.

'Stupid cow, I hope she chokes, blimey, nurse, what you got here, a Sherman Tank?'

Between us, we manipulate the bike up the steps and the first two flights of the wide stairs soon lie behind us.

'Thank you. I didn't know how I was going to do it.'

Now he smiles at me and I see his young brown handsome face and his teeth so white that they almost glitter in the dim light of the landing.

'That's OK, nurse, no problem, good luck with the delivery; I'd better get back to that old cow before she chokes to death.'

I hear his feet clatter down the marble stairs. The bike now leans against a cream wall whose paint stands out in flaking layers and the handlebars of the bike have just relieved it of some of its disfigurement.

My tap on the large ornate brown door, which had once admitted upstairs maids hastening to attend their lady's toiletry, brings the present lady of the house, or at least the lady of the room, to the door.

The young lady stands in the doorway in her nightdress, with a cardigan around her shoulders and, despite her advanced state of pregnancy, she still manages to look slim and rather elegant. She smiles and speaks in a quiet and pleasant voice as she steps back from the doorway.

'Come in, nurse, I'm pleased to see you, but I am sorry to bring you out on such a night.'

The words stop as her face grimaces, and her hands race to her large abdomen. I wheel the bike through the doorway as, without further word, she turns and walks back into the room.

'How often are the contractions coming?' I ask as I lean the bike beside the door and remove my bag.

She is sitting on the bed at the far side of the room and I can hardly see her, but I hear her.

'They are about every two minutes and they are very regular.'

I walk towards her. I am still wearing my outdoor coat but I can feel the cold. The room is large, in fact, from my small experience of living rooms or bedrooms, it seems to be a huge room. I had noted before how high the ceiling was, but now in just the light of a standard lamp, which stands at the far side of the room, it is hard to see where the ceiling starts. I had felt that the room was rather chilly when I visited yesterday, but now it feels positively frigid; maybe the wind has changed direction, and the draughts from the large window are blowing even stronger.

'Have you got any heat for the room, Mrs Wardle? I thought you had a fire.'

I had written 'gas fire' in the section on the notes marked 'Heating'.

She slides from the bed and passes me as she walks to the wall behind me. I follow her with my eyes. A large old gas fire stands in an enormous ornate fireplace, it is unlit. I stand beside her and look at the collapsed heap. I had not thought to look at the fire closely when I visited, but now it does not look at all adequate for the purpose. The elements of fireproof pottery, which should heat up in the gas flames, are broken and falling apart; no amount of flame will heat them in their present condition.

'It takes a lot of gas to warm it up, so I thought I'd wait until the baby is born before I put it on, you said that the baby would need a warm room.'

She smiles at me as she finishes speaking, and then looks

back at the dilapidated fire as if lost for words. I speak as a shudder runs through me.

'I think that we might need to warm things up a bit now, Mrs Wardle, before the baby arrives.'

She starts to speak again, but another contraction comes, and speech becomes impossible as I guide her to the bed. The contraction is long, and when it ends I leave her on the bed with a blanket over her and head towards the broken gas fire. With careful manipulation and the aid of an old pair of surgical forceps I resurrect two of the four elements of the fire. Blue flames rise and by the time I am back beside Mrs Wardle a red glow is showing. I can't really feel any heat at this side of the room but it looks cheerful. Her voice is quiet as a contraction ends.

'You'd better turn it off, nurse, I don't know how much money is left in the meter. My mother put a shilling in before she left, but I haven't got another one to put in.'

At the mention of her mother I realise that I have not yet seen her or Mrs Wardle's little boy. I had written on the notes *Mrs Wardle's mother will be with her daughter for the delivery and afterwards*. I ask her if this is still the case.

'Oh no, nurse, she came this afternoon, but she has gone back home, and taken my little boy with her. She'll be back tomorrow, and she'll bring some money then.'

We are on our own, Mrs Wardle and I. How had I made that mistake? I glance down at the notes, which I have placed on the dressing table. The next contraction comes close on the tail of its predecessor, the baby will soon be born, and we must have some heat. Where is her husband? Why isn't he here with some money? Why hadn't I checked on these things more carefully? We could all freeze in this room without some heat. I remember Mrs O'Reilly's hand extended towards the notes, I remember her sigh as, in my haste, I refuse any further discussion, and then I remember something else, the shilling in my coat pocket. I pray as I hold the shilling in my hand, 'Please don't do anything that needs a phone call,' and then my mind reminds me, there's no one to make a phone call if one is needed. So, what the heck, I think to myself as I hear the shilling ring its way into the meter.

7.10 p.m.

The contractions are close and regular, I must check if the baby is ready to come.

'Is there any water boiling, Mrs Wardle?'

She raises half to sitting and, without speaking, nods towards the fire. A small partition stands across the corner of the room near to it, a kettle stands on a gas ring behind this screen, and it is just warm. I light the gas beneath it as I look around for the water tap. I call out again as I put my head around the screen.

'Where is the sink, Mrs Wardle?'

For a moment there is silence, and then a small voice says, 'It's in the bathroom along the hall, nurse.'

I look across to where the woman is pulling hard on the gas and air machine, and my mind screams, 'No water.'

With saucepan in hand, I head for the door. As I open it, total blackness faces me. I turn to ask for help, but Mrs Wardle is still pulling hard on the gas and air. A distant glow shows as a light shines on one of the floors below, and I remember Errol had hit buttons on the walls as we climbed; the lights on the landings are on time switches. Holding the saucepan out beside me I creep along the wall, there must be a button near the top of the stairs. Momentarily the downward flight of stairs shows, and then the ground floor light clicks off. At the same moment, I hear the door behind me close, total blackness remains. My instinct is to turn and hurry back to the door, but for a moment the darkness disorientates me, and I am not sure in which direction to move. Light sweeps across the landing, a hand passes behind my head, and a strong smell of body odour tells me that someone stands behind me.

A voice, strong with a Midlands accent, says, 'They're a menace these timed lights, never give yo time to get anywhere afore they switch off, you all right there, nurse?'

The saucepan and my toes hang over the stairwell.

7.25 p.m.

A strongly built lady of forceful character has directed me to the bathroom at the end of the wide corridor.

'A disgrace is this place, used to be nice flats here, but things have gone downhill, the landlord doesn't care at all, he never sees the place, just sends someone to collect the rent, that's all he cares about.'

Tiles, once white, line the walls, they are grey and broken. A cracked china hand basin leans across the far corner of the large room, and an enormous iron bath with a grey interior stands under a high leaded window, its large lion's feet are the only part of it which still retain some of its original white paint.

Smiling across at me the large lady holds her hand out for the saucepan.

'You want water, nurse?'

Stepping over the water on the floor she pushes the pan under the large ornate tap, hits the pipe above the tap with a piece of metal, catches some of the water which gushes out into the bath, and then returns the pan to me.

Water bubbles in the saucepan, the baby is ready to be born. The room feels a little warmer, or maybe I am becoming used to the cold.

The baby girl is born without problems, and I wrap her in two cotton towels and a shawl before I hand her to her mother. Now I must head for the bathroom again as the baby needs her bath. But I know the tricks of the trade now, and this time there are no dark corridors. A tall thin man with long pale greasy hair is standing in the bathroom when I press the light button. He looks across at me with no apparent surprise as he finishes urinating into the bath. For a moment I am surprised, and am just starting to reprimand him for his behaviour when, without looking at me, he says, 'You want a bit darling, there's plenty for everyone, come and have a look.'

He holds his penis in his hand as he turns towards me, and the smell of alcohol drowns the smell of urine.

He continues his advance, his eyes bright with intoxication. Stepping sideways, I easily avoid his advance as I speak to him.

'You should be careful, sir, you might castrate yourself on that broken hand basin.'

For a long moment he stands and looks down at the dirty broken basin, and then, as if suddenly registering me, he turns and shouts, 'Oh we got a nursey worsey here have we. I love a uniform, show me a bit of black stocking, darling.'

He lunges towards me and, as I step sideways, he continues past me. His thighs hit the side of the metal bath and the upper part of his long body continues into it. The light clicks off, and in the prevailing darkness I hear him moan. I hit the light button, and as light fills the room again I look at his face. He is rather ashen but is still able to moan as he hangs over the bath. Neatly missing his head with the metal pipe I hit the tap and refill my saucepan. I leave as the water hitting the bottom of the bath throws urine up into his face, and I hear him coughing as I reach Mrs Wardle's door.

As I wash the baby by the fire I talk to Mrs Wardle. She is a graduate from London University and she had come to join her husband while he wrote his Doctorate at the local university. During his studies their son had been born, but when his wife had become pregnant again he had felt himself unable to take on the responsibilities of another child and had moved in with his research assistant who lives near the university. Mrs Wardle had found herself unable to pay the rent on the flat that she and her husband had rented, and she had moved to this cheaper accommodation only three weeks ago. Her husband had not been back to see her, but she still hopes that he will return. Her mother had come to her aid and had suggested that she move in with her, but she did not want to in case her husband did return.

9.45 p.m.

I leave Mrs Wardle lying in her bed at the far side of the room, and baby Ruth, wrapped in her shawl, sleeping in a crib a little closer to the fire. I had tried to get the baby as close to the fire as possible, but I dare not move her too far from her mother. As I close Mrs Wardle's door the light is on and a tall, thin pale-faced lady, with stringy hair, is helping my erstwhile suitor from the bathroom. He is still moaning, but she is silent.

As I leave to go home the wind has dropped a little and the snow has stopped, but the hill is difficult to climb, and as I dismount and start to push the bike, doubts come into my mind. I know that I should not have left Mrs Wardle alone. What if she bleeds? What if the baby chokes? The mother and baby are too far apart, she might not hear her baby.

Now I am swinging back into the front of the house. What can I do about the bike? I can't get it upstairs.

A voice behind me speaks.

'You not coming back for another baby are you, nurse?'

The drunken woman with peroxide-blond hair leans on Errol's arm and tries to focus on me. Errol pushes her off, and she staggers sideways.

'No, I just have to go back upstairs. The baby has been born, but I have to see the woman again for a minute.'

I stop speaking as I watch the woman sink slowly to the ground, Errol ignores her.

'You got to take that bike back up there again nurse, man you need to take a forklift truck around with you.'

I feel cold and despondent, I don't know what I need to do, but I do know I haven't got the money to ring the midwife, and I can't leave the woman and her baby alone.

'I don't really know yet, I've just got to go up to see what I can do.'

The brown eyes flash under the now not so low cap brim, and he smiles at me as he pulls the woman to her feet.

'You leave the bike with me, nurse. I'll put it by our door, we live on the ground floor, if anyone touches it there I'll see to them.'

Somehow I trust Errol and race up the stairs. I knock at the large brown door, ready to open it before Mrs Wardle can get out of bed, but am surprised as it is opened for me. A large figure confronts me. The lady, Mrs Hall, from across the landing stands in the doorway.

'Hello, nurse, you back?'

She smiles at me, and steps back into the room. The room has changed in the short time that I have been away. It has been transformed and now looks smaller and cosier. It takes a few moments for me to realise what has happened. The bed is now standing halfway across the room, and the baby lies close beside her mother. Mrs Hall speaks from behind me as she closes the door.

'Got George to move the bed, thought it might be a bit cold over there. Take such a lot of heating do these rooms, you have to sit on top of the fire to feel any warmth. Thought I might stay with her for a while. Joan says she wouldn't mind if I stayed.

She smiles across at Mrs Wardle who rests against her pillows, a cup of tea in her hands. Her face is quiet, and for the first time I see a little colour in her cheeks. Busying herself by the baby, Mrs Hall continues, 'If you like, nurse, I'll stay with her tonight. George is on nights, I might as well put my money in this meter and warm my legs by this fire as sit on my own, if that's all right with you, nurse.'

As she closes the door behind me the strong smell of body odour remains on the landing, but now I know that I can leave, I know that on the other side of the door kindness, in all its fragrances, lingers.

10.10 p.m.

Mrs O'Reilly's house seems to be in darkness as I climb the first flight of stairs, and clicking the light on in the clinical room I prop the gas and air machine by the wall and drop the used delivery bag on the floor. As I start to climb the second flight the smell of food hits me, and I realise that I am hungry, I have not eaten since lunch time. A note lies on the kitchen table.

'Out on a visit, food in oven.'

The gravy has dried to a dark brown ring around the edge of the pie, the mashed potatoes are dry and the peas are wrinkled, but, as I lift the plate from the warm oven, it looks like a feast. After only a few mouthfuls, I hear the front door close and footsteps sounding on the stairs. I know that they have stopped by the clinical door and I hastily push the food into my mouth as I anticipate Mrs O'Reilly's scold for not tidying up my equipment properly. The voice calls, 'Nurse Compton, would you come down here please?'

When I return to the kitchen the food is not only dry but also cold. As I face it for the second time Mrs O'Reilly looks at it, lifts the plate and scoops the food into the bin. A cheese sandwich and a cup of tea replace it.

3

Thursday 22nd March

2.30 a.m.

The bicycle bell rings in my dreams again, but this time my mind tells me what the ringing is and I am out of bed and standing by the telephone almost before my brain has woken up.

'Mrs O'Reilly's house, Pupil Midwife Compton speaking, may I help you?'

This time there is no hesitation as the voice, with a strong Irish accent, speaks out.

'Nurse, Mrs Murphy is going to have the baby, could you please come to the ground floor flat, number 12, Oakville Road.'

The call ends and I look around to see if Mrs O'Reilly is up, but I stand alone in the dark house; there is no sound from the floor below. Repeating the name over and over to myself I hastily dress and head down the stairs. I am the only sign of life. I look at my watch, I have been in bed for three and a half hours. As I look at the equipment I am thankful that I had spent the time to prepare it the previous night and now all is again ready for use.

I had visited Mrs Murphy last week and as I glance at the notes which I have retrieved from the drawer, I remind myself that this is her fourth child. Goodness, I had better hurry, this baby is not going to hang around.

I head for the stairs, no sound disturbs the darkness

and, laden with my equipment, I try to creep downstairs without putting on the light. My crash landing on the ground floor must have woken everyone.

The snow has stopped but the wind is still cold, and as I head once again downhill I am pleased to be wearing the thick stockings and a woollen scarf. This time I head away from the main road and the wheels spin past the scratched and scraped trunks of cherry trees, which, I have been told, will be a picture in a couple of months. The Murphy's, like my midwife, live in a part of what used to be one large house in the rich, residential area of this once prosperous city. The houses are not as large as the ones facing the main road and most of them have received better care, but the increase in population and the introduction of the combustion engine have created havoc in these once sedate and quiet streets. The night is dark. I have managed to navigate by following the trees, but have been unable to see any road names, that is if there are any left to see after the local youths have finished with them.

3.10 a.m.

I am lost. The snow starts again and I stand at a junction and stare into darkness. The rows of houses at each side of the road have ended, all I can see is snow as I look to my left and to my right. I know that the Murphys' house stands on the left-hand side on one of the long, downhill, roads. Have I passed the house, or did I turn down the wrong road? I climb off the bike and, pushing it to the pavement edge, lean over and look closely at the piece of road sign which clings to the low stone wall. Half the sign remains and I can just read the word Beech; I have ridden down Beechville Road. Standing upright I try to visualise the road map. I am supposed to bring this with me, but I know it lies on the table in my room. Mrs O'Reilly lives at the top of Forest Hill, I am sure that Oakville is the road next to it, but maybe I am wrong. I will have to turn right at this junction and see if the next road along is Oakville. I push the bike up the hill, I have been unable to find any road signs, but light shows in a downstairs window, and praying that this is number 14 Oakville Road, I head for the gate. As I wheel the bike up the steps to the house the door opens and a man in a large jumper stands at the door. Without speaking he waves me into the house and, taking the handlebars of the bike, he almost whispers, 'You'd better hurry along in now, I think that we are nearly there.'

I haven't got my breath yet, so without speaking, and hoping that this is the right house, I set to work with as much haste as I can muster. I grab the delivery bag and, releasing the gas and air box from its retaining strap, I drag it along the passageway and head for the room to which I am being directed. The room is brightly lit and light reflects from the polished linoleum floor. A bed lies in the far corner of the room and I head towards it, swinging the gas and air machine box ahead of me. I have not seen the rug which lies at the foot of the bed, and as the heavy box and my foot land on the rug together they set it in motion. Across the shining linoleum the rug and the box shoot. I, with legs wobbly from lack of sleep and uphill riding, am caught off balance. I throw the delivery bag away from me and fight to stand, but down I go. The rug stops travelling when my body, which lies on it, gets wedged under the bed. The last ounce of breath is knocked out of me, and my head hits the gas and air machine as I come to a standstill. The mattress presses down on my back, and I can see Mrs Murphy's face as she looks at me over the side of the bed. I hear Mr Murphy's voice somewhere above me.

'Where's the nurse gone, Mary? I just let her in. Where did she go?'

Still looking at me over the side of the bed, Mrs Murphy bursts out laughing.

'She's under the bed here, Patrick.'

Mr Murphy's legs bend and his face appears by that of his wife.

'You all right there then, nurse?' he asks.

I am anything but all right, I cannot move, and I call out as loudly as I can from my cramped position, 'Mr Murphy, could you please pull the mat out from under the bed?'

The hand pulls at my coat, it pulls at my dress and with much apologising he pulls at my legs, but there is no movement. The voice calls out, 'I can't get hold of the mat nurse, you are laying on it.'

I try to move, but I can't, I'm wedged. Mrs Murphy continues to laugh, and her not inconsiderable weight rocks the bed up and down. I also hear her call that she must push.

'Mr Murphy, you will have to pull me out by my legs.'

So after many muffled instructions, some to Mrs Murphy to stop pushing, and some to Mr Murphy to keep pulling, I emerge from under the bed. The gas and air machine, the perpetrator of the crime, does not make it, it remains under the bed. But I do not need to recover it as Mrs Murphy is laughing so much that the baby is born with little intervention from me, and it is with continuing delight that Mrs Murphy receives her daughter in her arms in double-quick time.

'Nurse, you've given us everything, look at your daughter, Pat.

Mr Murphy stands to attention at the side of his wife with just a little smile on his face. I know from the notes that he already has four sons, so I think, to him, this just looks like another mouth to feed. But his wife's joy continues unabated as she gazes at her daughter.

'At last, a girl. We can't call her Mary, everybody is named Mary, although I know we told your mother that we would call her Mary if it was a girl.'

She hesitates for a moment and then continues, 'I know, I shall call her Joy, she was born with so much joy it is the only name for her.'

3.30 a.m.

Apart from some rather wrinkled forty denier stockings, I am now restored to my equilibrium and set about recording the relevant events and times of the delivery. I manage to omit to mention that many of my instructions had been delivered from under the bed on which my patient was lying, and not while I was standing by her side. Baby Joy lies in her crib, Mrs Murphy sits against her pillows, and Mr Murphy has retired to the kitchen to make a nice cup of tea.

'Would you like a drink, nurse?' I hear Mr Murphy's voice call from the centre of the room and, without looking up from the notes, I reply, 'Yes please, Mr Murphy, I would love a drink.'

As tea is being served I had assumed that I would be offered a cup or a mug of tea, but when I looked up I am amazed to see Mr Murphy's extended hand holding a glass of clear fluid. For a moment I hesitate and my eyes stray towards his wife's tray of tea; a cup of tea would be more welcome than a glass of water. But Mr Murphy looks very pleased with his offer, and I do not wish to offend him. I can get a cup of tea and something to eat at the midwife's flat, so I take the glass and, being quite thirsty, I take a large swallow.

It takes Mr Murphy about ten minutes to get me

breathing normally again. The clear fluid had been a celebration drink, a gift from Mr Murphy to thank me for delivering him a daughter; it was a glass of his precious Irish whiskey.

3.50 a.m.

All is calm again, and baby Joy lies awaiting her turn for attention.

'I've put the bath of water by the fire in the front room, nurse, thought you would be more comfortable there.'

The rather chipped, enamel baby bath stands on a low table beside a huge, bright fire, which burns in a large stone fireplace. The red glow lights up the room, and a table lamp throws light across a well-worn armchair, which does its best to soak up all of the warmth of the fire. No need to worry about the baby being cold here, I think. The baby's crib stands beside the armchair, and I am profuse in my assurance to Mr Murphy that these conditions are exactly right, and that he can do nothing more now than ensure that his wife rests. Baby Joy is a fine strong baby who enjoys her first bath, and we talk and chatter as she waves her arms around and pulls faces in reply to my comments and questions. She is bathed and the remains of her umbilical cord are dressed.

5.10 a.m.

'Would you like another cup of tea, nurse?'

I look up into the face of Mr Murphy. He smiles as he extends a cup and saucer towards me.

With a start I sit up. I am in my delivery gown, and on my lap something warm and soft moves. With dawning realisation I panic; I had fallen asleep with the baby on my lap. The delivery gown is wrapped around her, and with near panic hitting my brain, I lift the cloth. Baby Joy, lying face down across my lap, responds to the insult of so sudden a blast of cold air. With her arms stretching out over her head and legs extending outwards she cries out. Trying to remain calm I attempt to speak, but no voice comes. Eventually, after some coughing, I manage a few words as I gather the baby in my arms.

'Thank you, Mr Murphy.'

Trying to sound casual, and to give the impression that midwives always sleep while they are caring for the baby, I ask, 'Is your wife asleep, Mr Murphy?'

He leans over, and puts a piece of wood on the fire, which is now burning low, as he speaks.

'Yes she's fine, sleeping as well as the baby was.'

He looks at me and smiles.

'Came in earlier to see if you wanted anything, but you all looked so comfortable. I thought I'd better come in now though, thought the fire might be burning low.' So saying, he throws another piece of wood on the embers, and leaves the room.

5.40 a.m.

The baby is feeding at her mother's breast, and I have everything ready for my departure; the gas and air machine has been recovered, and the mat has been re-placed at the foot of the bed. Now Mr Murphy carries the offending machine into the hall.

'Have you got to carry all this lot on that bike?' he asks.

Without waiting for a reply he says, 'Let me give you a lift, I've got the vehicle parked just down the road, it will only take a minute to fetch it.'

'What about my bike?' I ask his retreating form.

He speaks as he retrieves a large set of keys which were hanging on a nail, 'I can put the bike up on the back.'

I hear the roar of the engine, and I'm sure I feel the floor shake as gears grind. The roar sounds louder as Mr Murphy throws open the hall door and takes hold of the gas and air machine. Without speaking to me he heads through the front door and down the steps. The monster stands by the kerb; well, it stands by the kerbs on both sides of the road. The yellow cab stands high off the ground, and behind it and attached to it stands a yellow trailer with a tractor on it. Seizing the bike, Mr Murphy disappears behind the tractor, and after a few moments he looks down at me from the high cabin. I had expected a lorry, or a van, but this is a moving circus.

'Want a hand up, nurse?'

Mr Murphy leans across the cabin and lets the door on the pavement side fall open. For a moment I am lost for words. How can we take this enormous vehicle through the back streets of the city at this hour in the morning? I try to make my excuses for not riding in the lorry.

'The journey is not long; I can soon ride it, Mr Murphy.'

But the bike has gone, and there is nothing for it but to haul myself up into the cabin beside him. With all my effort and some pulling from Mr Murphy, I gain my seat high up beside the driver. With what seems to be a great deal of gear changing, we are off. There are a few cars parked at the side of the road but Mr Murphy seems to take all in his stride as we head down the hill.

'I live at the top of Greenwood Hill.'

I speak in jerks as I hang onto the side of the seat. My feet don't reach the ground and the seat is large and I slide across it at every corner.

'Yes, I know where your road is, nurse, but I have to go this way so that I can get through. I have to do a whole circuit so that I can get back to the parking spot.'

He smiles across at me as his large hands, on the ends of

sinewy arms, spin the steering wheel. We do the circuit, and the whole of the suburb is woken. No oversleeping for anyone this morning. As Mr Murphy lifts my bicycle down from behind the large yellow earth mover I see Mrs O'Reilly's curtains move.

'Sorry she's not a Rolls Royce, nurse, but she's a fine girl.'

Smiling at me, Mr Murphy gives his yellow girlfriend a loving pat, and swings into her cab. With a grinding of gears and revving that completes the morning call, he sets off.

10.30 a.m.

'Go on then, knock at the door.'

I swing my legs out of Mrs O'Reilly's low-slung Austin car. Half asleep I had watched the pebbles on the road rush by beneath her feet as she changed gear a little more quietly than had Mr Murphy. Now we are outside the Murphy's house, and I must raise my tired body and push it on to the next job. I am not looking forward to this visit, Mrs O'Reilly always does the first recall visit with me and Mrs Murphy and baby Joy will be fine I am sure, but I am dreading having to answer for my catalogue of mistakes and misdemeanors. A boy of about nine years of age answers the door. He snuffles loudly, and makes an attempt to pull up his wrinkled sock when he sees me. He shouts over his shoulder, 'It's the nurse, Mammy'.

A muffled voice replies, 'Then let her in, Sean, don't keep her standing at the door.'

'There's two of them, Mammy.'

Sean doesn't have time to wait for a reply. Mrs O'Reilly puts her hand on his head, spins him around and, taking him into the house with her, she asks, 'And where's the Mammy lying then?'

The reply comes.

'I'm in here, nurse.'

The passageway is as I remembered it, long with a well-polished floor. The door at its end opens into a bedroom and the mat lies on the glistening linoleum at the foot of the bed.

Mrs Murphy and baby Joy are declared fit and all is well. Mrs Murphy declares, 'I've had four confinements now nurse and I can honestly say that this was by far the easiest of them. Nurse Compton there never gave any of us time to start thinking about pain, she just made things move along.'

Mrs O'Reilly looks up at Mrs Murphy's face as she finishes examining her abdomen and, pulling the blanket back over her patient, she picks up the notes which lie in an envelope on the bedside table.

'Did she then.'

She mumbles and speaks to the notes as she asks, 'No gas and air given then, nurse?'

Before I have time to attempt an explanation, Mrs Murphy's voice intercedes.

'Goodness no, Mrs O'Reilly, by the time nurse had got everything set up, I was pushing, Miss Joy here was eager to get out and start some feeding. A great feeder she is, Mrs O'Reilly.'

Mrs O'Reilly is still examining the notes and, looking up over her glasses, she beckons me over.

'Quite a long time between your arrival and the delivery.'

She turns the notes over as if seeking for some hidden information.

'I see no record of any examination either internal or external, did you do an examination? Have you forgotten to record it?'

Now I am caught, I had done no examination because I

was lying under the bed. Mrs Murphy's voice rings out, 'Lord love us, nurse, don't say you've forgotten.'

For a moment my head spins, how am I going to explain my not saying what had happened? It is paramount to lying. Mrs Murphy is speaking again.

'I was sure that I wanted to go to the toilet when nurse arrived, she said that I really wanted to push the baby out, so she insisted on coming to the toilet with me.'

She looks across at my white face, and smiles.

'She was right, and by the time I got back to the bed the baby was there.'

Mrs O'Reilly looks at her over the notes, and then turns just her eyes to my now scarlet face.

'Hmm,' she says as she turns her eyes back to the notes.

'It took you a long time to attend to the baby and clear up, was there a problem?'

'No, no problem, I was just having a drink and a chat with Mr Murphy.'

The memory of the whiskey almost takes my breath away, and I hope that Mr Murphy does not appear to deny my explanation of events. Mrs O'Reilly speaks as she lifts her eyes from the notes, 'It must have been some chat!'

Putting the notes back on the table she turns and smiles at Mrs Murphy.

'Well everything looks fine, Mrs Murphy, and congratulations on getting a girl. Write the notes, nurse, and we'll go and leave Mrs Murphy in peace.

Sean peers around the door, and two small faces look out under his arm.

'Is there anyone to be with you, Mrs Murphy? I don't think that young Sean is quite old enough to be of much help.'

Mrs Murphy pulls herself up the bed and hitches herself

sideways. I feel sure that she has already been out of bed looking after the house.

'My husband will be back shortly, just has to do a delivery with the lorry.'

I later find out that the lorry's delivery was over fifty miles away.

Mrs O'Reilly and I sit in her car. She pulls the starter and, after a couple of false starts and a bit of extra choke, we are off up the hill.

'There are some yawning gaps in those case notes, Nurse Compton. It was a normal delivery so you will have to put it in your Case Book, but I don't know how you are going to explain the sequence of events to your tutor.'

Holding her head high as she manipulates the small car around a large puddle which extends out from the side of the road, she continues, 'Or maybe you think that she is even more gullible than I am.'

4

Saturday 24th March

8.30 a.m.

I open my eyes slowly. Light from the window shines on my face, and the crucifix lies in daylight. This is the first time I have woken and seen it in the light. For a moment I look at the cross with the almost skeletal figure hanging from it. Then my mind asks me, 'Why are you still in bed?' Throwing the blankets off I sit up quickly, probably too quickly as my head feels dizzy. I glare at my watch and try to get it into focus. Eight thirty, what am I thinking of? Then I remember, this is my day off. No deliveries are due in the next few days so Mrs O'Reilly and I had decided that I should take my day off. Mrs O'Reilly is sitting in the kitchen reading her newspaper, her uniform dress is crisp and clean. She looks up at me, says 'Good morning' and then continues with her reading. I sit down and help myself to some cornflakes; she looks at me over the top of her paper.

'Are you going out today?'

She smiles at me – well I take it for a smile and so smile back as I reply, 'I might go and look at the shops this morning, and I'm going back to the hospital this evening to meet a friend.'

She speaks over the top of her paper again.

'What time do you think that you will be back? I ask because officially you will be on call from midnight, I thought I'd make the point just in case you were off to one of those all-night do's that young people go to these days.'

I had never been to an all-night do, and didn't think that I would have the energy to go to one now, even if I did know where to find one.

'I'm going to the Students' Union Dance at the university, so I should be back just after eleven.'

Without speaking she rises, looks at her pocket watch, puts it back in her uniform pocket, folds her paper, and is gone.

7.30 p.m.

It was raining hard when I got off the bus, and now I feel like a drowned rat. My hair is cut very short so rain is no great concern to me. However, I have struggled to obtain the straight look which is in fashion, and with the aid of a good deal of spray, which felt like glue, I had succeeded to some extent. But the rain has done its worst and strands of hair now spring up in places where they are not needed.

As I stand inside the main entrance to the Students' Union building the usual noise assails the ears. Clutter fills every available space and all the walls are coated with notices which announce, threaten, offer, sell, or generally inform those who read them. The entrance to the ladies' cloakroom is crowded, but inside it is almost empty. Three rickety hand basins stand facing the room; they are attached to the wall behind the door, and above them are spotty unlit mirrors. Hanging my coat on one of the pegs that line the far side of the room, I return to a mirror and try to control the hair, but not having the right equipment available, I fail. A young woman, who stands two mirrors away from me, fills the air with a cloud of spray from a can. I sneeze and retreat. A toilet flushes and a young woman in heels so high that she can hardly walk totters out from one of the two cubicles. She joins her friend at the mirror, and without attempting to wash her hands she starts to apply various cosmetics. The door bursts open and three girls walk in, they talk loudly and shake rain from their coats. Running my hands through my hair I release it from the restraining glue, and the curls spring back. I check that my stocking seams are straight and that the slit in my dark green pencil skirt is centre back, and exit.

The passageway is ill lit, people come and go, and damp coats hang from the walls. I hear Bill Haley rocking around the clock long before I enter the room. The dance hall-cum-theatre is crowded, and the noise of the music is deafening. I can't see far into the room, and people squeeze past me blocking my view even further. The music stops, and the silence is almost deafening. Two young men stand on the stage at the far end of the long room. They have their heads together over a cardboard box, one lifts a record from the box and they both look at it. It comes out of its sleeve, and the quiet of the room is gone as Little Richard lets rip. I look around but see no one I know. Above me a balcony rises, and I know that refreshments are sold here. I have arranged to meet Tony at the dance, and I tell myself that maybe he is on the balcony. Tony is a medical student; he and I had met at the Union when I was doing my three months midwifery in the hospital. I had not known that he was a medical student, and would probably not have started the relationship had I known. I had worked with doctors for some years, and had always found then to be egotistical and fond of themselves. However, Tony and I have been meeting for over two months now.

The balcony is crowded, it is almost impossible to see anyone. I collide into the back of a tall young man, and he turns and catches me as I stumble forward.

'I'm very sorry.'

I speak as I regain my balance, and for a moment I look up into his face. There is something about the face that I recognise. He has shoulder-length brown hair, and a small goatee beard. No, I don't know him. Smiling, I step away from him, then a voice with a familiar accent calls, 'Is that Dot? Are you Dot Compton? You must be Dot.'

I smile weakly, maybe he is the relative of a patient.

'Yes, I'm Dot Compton, I'm afraid I don't know . . . My goodness, is it Alan, is it Alan Bunting?'

Now I can see beyond the long hair and the beard, and I recognise my old school friend.

'Goodness, Dot, fancy seeing you here, are you at the university? What are you studying? I didn't know they had a maths course running. Well, well, well!'

I had known Alan when I was at school. On many occasions he and I had competed for top place in maths. I had seen little of him since I had left Stonemore Grammar School but I knew he had stayed on at school and had gone to university. Now I hear myself speaking as he clasps his arm around my shoulder and steers me away from the throng.

'Are you studying here, Alan? I haven't seen you here before.'

He is now even taller than I remember, but the friendly smile and the bright eyes have not changed at all; maybe there is a little more hair around the smile, but the smile is just the same.

'So what gives?' he asks when we can hear without having to scream at each other.

I repeat my question, this time he answers.

'Well not actually studying, I'm doing some post-graduate work, I suppose you can call it studying, I've just started my doctorate, just got it registered. But you, what are you doing here?'

Two people push past us, and my answer is lost in the confusion, at least I think that it is lost until I hear him say with incredulity, 'A midwife, did I hear you right? A midwife, you mean someone who delivers babies?'

For some reason I am blushing as if I am ashamed of my profession, or maybe I am ashamed that he has moved so far away from me academically. A voice calls out behind me, 'Al, I've been looking everywhere for you. Where have you been? Come on, Stew has arrived.'

A tall girl, with blond hair tied back with a piece of black string, swings between us. Alan stops her progress with his arm, and she halts beside him hanging onto his arm to still her movement. He moves his hand up and down as if to still her agitated movements and, half turning his face, he kisses her on the top of her head as, still looking at me, he says, 'Jude, I want you to meet Dot. You remember Dot, I told you about her, my chief maths competitor at school. She's delivering babies now.'

For the first time she looks at me and, clutching Alan's arm even closer, says, 'Hmm, I always imagined you to be six foot tall with a black moustache. Al darling, do come before I lose sight of Stew in this crush.'

For a moment he looks at me and then, bending towards her, he moves off sideways.

'Bye, Dot, see you around, good luck with the babies.'

Tony does not turn up – at least I don't see him – but I catch sight of Maureen on the side of the dance floor and I am just about to call out to her when a young woman walks over, and claims her arm in familiar fashion.

11.15 p.m.

Mrs O'Reilly's house is in darkness when I arrive back, and the icy wind returns as I climb the dark steps. I feel flat and depressed. It had not always been my intention to be a midwife, and now I have been reminded of what I might have been. Mathematics had been my sole interest at school, and there had been every possibility that I would obtain a good university place to continue my studies. But my father had different ideas. I am his only daughter, and as far as he was concerned going to university was not on the agenda. Alan Bunting had been an integral part of my life during the years I had hoped to forget. Now, as I squeeze past the old black bike, my present life seems unimportant and meaningless. What am I doing here, riding around on this black monstrosity in the middle of the night? Why am I not studying and reading for my doctorate?

I fall asleep with a headache, and tears of self-pity roll onto my pillow.

5

Sunday 25th March

3.30 a.m.

The bell is ringing through my dreams again, now it wakens me even when I am in a deep sleep. My eyes feel swollen, and it takes some seconds to un-glue them enough to see, but I know where the phone is and, with eyes still closed, I speak.

'Midwife O'Reilly's house, Pupil Midwife Compton speaking. Can I help you?'

'Has that other woman had a girl yet?'

For a moment I'm not sure if I have heard correctly.

'Could you speak up please, I can't hear what you are saying.'

The agitated voice now shouts, 'Has the other woman had the girl yet, only we want a boy and my wife says that she isn't going to have the baby until the other woman has had a girl.'

For a moment I stand and look at the phone, I do not know what the man is talking about. I hear his voice shouting over the phone again.

'Are you there, nurse? You told my wife that you always deliver in threes, three girls followed by three boys. My wife doesn't want to have a girl, so have you delivered the third girl?'

Now everything comes back to me. As a joke I had told the women at the antenatal clinic that I had a routine, I deliver three babies of one sex and then change to the other sex. It had been a bit rich of me as, at the time, I had only delivered two babies, however they had both been girls. As I have since delivered another girl, I am able to calm the gentleman's fears without a lie.

'Yes, sir, I have delivered the third girl.'

Before I can say anything else, he shouts, 'Oh that's good, because, you see, the wife has been going strong for some time now, but she wanted to give you time to deliver the third girl before she sends for you.'

The line goes quiet, and I almost scream into the mouthpiece, 'What is your wife's name?'

He comes back on the line and, as if as a second thought, adds, 'Oh, its Mrs West, nurse, you know, Mrs West.'

The line goes quiet, and then as a second, second thought, he says, 'Bye, nurse, see you.'

I hold the now silent earpiece; my eyes are still glued half-closed, but now they snap open as I remember Mrs West. She is a forceful lady in her middle thirties who has three daughters, the eldest being about thirteen years old and the youngest eight. This pregnancy had been a bit of a shock, I think as much a shock to Mr West as it has been to Mrs West. On several occasions she had informed the ladies gathering at antenatal clinic that she didn't think he still had it in him.

And, eavesdropping on the conversation at the antenatal clinic, I had come to the conclusion that Mr West's future could become uncertain if Mrs West had another girl. To reassure herself that she carried a male child she had visited a clairvoyant and this good lady had assured her that only boys are conceived at a particular date and moment in time. Mrs West had been able to place the event of the child's conception on the astrological calendar with an accuracy known only to astronomers, identifying the date of the next Halley's Comet, and so she was quite certain that she would have a boy. Gold rings had been hung over the distended abdomen, all had turned in the direction denoting a male child's presence in the amniotic sac, and I, in my naivety, had joined in the affray with my claim to know the sex of the child by where in my magic sequence it was to be born.

3.45 a.m.

Throwing my leg over the saddle and sliding my hands into my newly acquired lambskin gloves, I set off down the hill hoping against hope that the extent of my stupidity would not be compounded by Mrs West, or her child, getting into trouble because of a delay in calling me. As the wind hits me I cannot believe that she and her husband had believed this silly superstition. With coat flying, I whirl into a road of detached houses with pretentious bay windows. The door opens before I knock, and light floods the short pathway and tiny garden. A tall thin pale girl stands beside the door which she holds open. Before I can speak, a man, who is obviously the father of the girl as the only facial feature that differs between them is the father's black pencil moustache, comes down the stairs two at a time. Putting his hand behind me he almost pushes me up the stairs.

'You go up, nurse, I'll bring your things up.'

He is out of the door and claiming the bike, and with the same urgency I head up the stairs two at a time.

Mrs West is laying on the bed, not a stitch of clothing covers her. Sweat runs down her face, and her hands, which cling onto to her large abdomen, look as though they are hanging onto the child within it.

'Oh, nurse, is it true you've delivered the third girl?'

'Yes,' I almost shout as I hurry towards her.

With a great sigh she leans back against the pillows, raises her arms, and pushes. The amniotic sac bursts, and for the second time that morning my eyes are glued together. The baby is born, and my beautiful new lambskin gloves receive it with all the tender care they can manage.

Mrs West sits up and looks at her baby and, as if with her last breath, she gasps, 'What have I got, what is it, nurse?'

Ignoring her cries, I fight to remove my now soaked lambskin gloves and, throwing them onto the floor behind me, I turn to the large young gentleman who lies in flaccid state before me. Lifting him by his feet I blow into his face. No cry sounds.

'It's a boy! Arthur, it's a boy, thank you, nurse, I had faith in you, look, Arthur, the nurse has got a boy for us.'

Arthur has just made it upstairs with the delivery bag. Again ignoring Mrs West, I shout over her cries.

'Mr West, bring my bag over here as quickly as you can.'

He holds the bag in one hand, and the gas and air machine in the other as he looks around for somewhere to place the machine. I wave him towards me with one hand, and with the other I rub the legs of the still child.

'Throw the box on the floor and get the bag to me, quickly.'

Now the lack of preparation tells, nothing is where it should be, and the baby has been born too quickly.

The father stands beside me, the bag in his hand, and a frightened look on his face.

'Put it on the bed and open it, please.'

I am speaking down towards the baby as I continue to rub his legs and arms. Pulling the bag towards me I turn it around, push up the sleeves of my mac, and reach into the bag. No time for the niceties of sterility. I throw a dressing towel across the mother's leg, delve into the depths of the bag and seize a pair of forceps to clamp the cord twice. I grab the first piece of material which comes to hand, which turns out to be a piece of cotton wool, to support the cord and release the child from his mother. Mrs West's voice sounds breathless and hushed as she watches my actions over her deflated abdomen and asks, 'Is he all right nurse? Is something wrong with him?'

Mr West comes to my aid and, as I glance up, I see his now very pale face appear beside that of his wife.

'No there's nothing wrong, dear, the nurse is just looking after him, you know what men are like, always slow in getting going.'

Mrs West looks up at him and, smiling, touches his face. He bends over her and kisses her forehead.

The baby lies pale and immobile, in this world but not a part of it. Pushing my sleeves back up again, I reach over to the bag. It is full, as full it had been when I had so carefully packed it. The equipment for caring for the baby still lies in its depths. Sterility has already gone by the board, so tipping up the large black bag, I pour its contents onto the now damp bed sheet. The small red rubber catheter comes to the top of the pile and, seizing it, I put one end of it in the baby's mouth and I suck at the other end. There is the sound of mucous being removed, but the baby does not respond. I lift him by his feet and rub their soft pink soles with my thumb, but still there is no life, the well-formed and potentially strong body does not live. One of the midwives I had worked with in the hospital had always put the baby across its mother's leg. I lift the slippery flaccid body. Did she lay the infant head high or head low? Just do it, my mind screams. I place him on the towel which lies across his mother's ample thigh, and I push the catheter in his nose. The upper lip rises as if in disdain at this assault, and then the nostrils extend and the mouth stretches. Master James Arthur West lets the world know who he is in no uncertain tones, and his father cries with him; the sleeves of his white office shirt will never be the same again.

4.35 a.m.

The room is suddenly full of people; two young girls dance around the bed, the neighbour follows Mr West up the stairs, and it seems that the whole road is outside and celebrating. Mrs West leans against her pillows holding her fine strong son, and the neighbour marvels at my ability to produce a child of a certain sex according to its place in my delivery schedule. I try to explain that I have no control and the possibility of Mr West having a greater part in this determination than I, but my protestations go unheeded. The notes again look rather lopsided as I write them; I will have to discuss what to write in the section requesting information about the pre-birth examinations, but I think that Mrs O'Reilly, like me, is starting to run out of plausible explanations.

5.00 a.m.

I turn baby James over on my knee and he looks at me with an accusing eye, which seems to say, 'You took your time in coming, I thought that I was going to get squashed to death in there.'

I speak my apology out loud as I wipe him on the delivery gown which I have just managed to get into.

'Sorry about that, young man, teach me to mind my tongue in future, and not to play silly games with people.'

He opens and closes his mouth and waves his arms in the air. I place a finger in his hand, and his fingers close around it in an iron grasp.

'Nothing wrong with your grasp on life now that you've got going, is there young man?'

Mr West stands behind me.

'Is there something you need, nurse?'

'No, Mr West,' I reply. 'I was just having a chat with your big fine son here, just checking that he knows how to hang onto life now that he's got it.'

He smiles, I think the first smile that I have seen and, as he gently touches the top of his son's head, I ask, 'Would you like to hold him, Mr West?'

He steps backwards as if stung.

'Oh no, no, no, nurse, I couldn't do that, I might hurt him.'

I smile up at him as I wrap his son back in the dressing towel and stand up. I hold the child out towards him.

'Come on, Mr West, this is your son we are talking about here, only you can teach him how to be a man, and you've got to start by saying hello.'

Holding his son in his arms as he turns his back on me, his words sound muffled. 'If I cry much more tonight, he'll have the right to question my gender.'

He returns the child to me, and speaks as he bends over.

'Thank you for coming so quickly nurse, and for doing what you did. My wife is a very strong-willed woman, and I could not move her from that silly superstition once she had got it in her head.'

I start to say that it was my fault for planting the idea, but he stops me.

'I just want to say thank goodness it was you, a clear thinker with an ordered mind. Don't you ever let anyone tell you that you don't have the best job in the world.'

After touching my shoulder for a moment, he turns and is gone.

I look down at baby James; he purses his lips and nods

his head, obviously he is already in agreement with his father.

The face of Alan Bunting swims before my eyes, and laughing I ask my young ward, 'What good are dry old numbers anyway, eh?'

His arms shoot upwards and his legs shoot out as, shivering and shaking, he sinks into his warm bath and his eyes say, 'Dead right there, Dot, nothing to beat your first good bath.'

6

Thursday 29th March

6.00 p.m.

Down the hill I fly again. The rain has stopped but the bicycle tyres swish loudly through the puddles. There is little daylight left, but I can't be bothered to switch on my lights. I should have done this visit much earlier in the day but I had spent half the day visiting Mrs White, a woman who seemed to go out of labour every time I walked through her door. I have ridden to Mrs White's semi-detached house four times during the day, but the baby has not been born, and now I am exhausted. Her husband had telephoned again just as I was leaving the house, but I couldn't make the visit as I have to make the final call on Mrs Burns some time today, and that some time must be before the family settle down for the evening. Baby Elizabeth is now ten days old and I must make my last check of mother and baby, enter my findings in the notes and return them to Mrs O'Reilly. I must also complete the case in my own Case Book. I went back to see my tutor at the hospital yesterday and I was the only pupil who didn't have a completed case recorded. The tutor had said that if I continued at this speed I would find myself unable to enter for the final exam. Maureen, of course, had already completed two cases and, as she had told me on every possible occasion, the third would be completed tomorrow.

I hope that if I can put on some speed I will be able to see Mrs Burns and get back before Mrs White delivers. However, now I face an unknown for as I was leaving, Mrs O'Reilly had pushed notes into my hand saying, 'This lady booked with Mrs Quinn in November, and we don't seem to have seen much of her since then. She lives just around the corner from Mrs Burns, could you knock and ask if she still lives at the same address?'

I hadn't looked at the notes before I left, and now, as I see the top of them sticking out of my bag, I feel imposed upon and annoyed. I am determined that this visit will be a quick knock at a door, a question, a *yes* or *no* answer, back on the bike and off. I have no intention of missing a delivery.

True to form, Mrs Burns is well. Baby Elizabeth has a few spots on her face, but she is fit and rosy. It has taken little time to complete all the formalities. Now, as I push the completed notes into the bag, the other notes come to hand and I lift them out to look at the address as I ask, 'Do you know where Silver Street is by any chance, Mrs Burns?'

She looks up from the cot where she attends to the baby and her eyes rest on my face for some moments before she speaks.

'What do you want to know about that place for, nurse?'

For a moment I hesitate and look back at the notes. Yes, the address is 14 Silver Street.

Offering Mrs Burns my most professional smile and tone of voice, I reply, 'I must make a visit.'

Someone coughs behind me. I hadn't heard Mr Burns enter the room; he had been sitting in the kitchen reading the *Racing Times* when I arrived, but now he stands behind me and the paper hangs from his hand as he asks, 'You going to Silver Street now, nurse?'

Looking up from my bag, I again offer what I think is

my confident and professional smile, as I reply, 'If you will be kind enough to tell me where it is, Mr Burns, I will be off there.'

He stands across the doorway as I approach him, and makes no attempt to move.

'Couldn't you go tomorrow morning, nurse, I mean in daylight.'

His face looks quite red, and Mrs Burns comes across and pulls at his arm.

'Come on, George, I'm sure nurse knows what she is doing, and if somebody needs her now then they need her now and not tomorrow morning, now don't they?'

He presses his lips together tightly as he looks at me and his voice is sharp as he speaks.

'You go and do what you got to do, nurse, but don't you go hanging around there, if there's any nonsense you come back and give this door a knock, and I'll come down.'

Mrs Burns squeezes his arm and smiles up at his face. Mr Burns turns and, treading heavily on each wooden step, he precedes me to the pavement. Mrs Megs is in the hallway, I can see her face peering over Mr Burns' shoulder. After directing me to Silver Street, the man remains at the pavement edge and I raise my hand to him as I swing my bicycle into a side street.

6.35 p.m.

Following his instructions I arrive on Silver Street. As I ride up to it, number 14 looks quite ordinary. The door, with its flaking paint, stands firmly closed, and the curtains are drawn across the window. Climbing off the bike, I lift its front wheel onto the pavement and head towards the door. Three young men, who I had just passed, now catch up with me. Their raucous voices

silence as they descend on me in a flock. One takes hold of
the handlebars of the bike, and he pulls it to a halt, the
second comes up behind me and whistles as he rubs his
hand across my buttocks, the third makes a wide circle
around the bike as he looks me up and down and, speaking through the cigarette, which he has clasped in his
teeth, he asks, 'You going in there, darling? You going to
be in there tonight?'

I grasp the handlebars and the front wheel of the bike
swings around and hits the man who is bending forward.
He falls back laughing as he shouts, 'Wow, and rough too.'

For a moment I am overwhelmed, then, making my
voice as stern as I can manage under these conditions, I
call out, 'Do you mind moving? I have business to attend
to in these premises.'

There is a roar of laughter as both I and my bike are
pushed across the pavement, and a voice roars out, 'Don't
we all, darling.'

With the hand still clasping my buttock, I am propelled
through the door and into a narrow hallway. The three
young men come with me. A staircase faces me. In the
semi-darkness I can see two men sitting on the stairs, and
in my perturbation I bump into a large man who stands in
the hall and leans on the banister rail. Without speaking,
the large man puts his arm across in front of the three
advancing youths who come to a sudden halt and I
continue on to the base of the stairs. For a moment I
stand confused and breathless. The youths retreat back
through the open door which slams shut behind them,
and the large man returns to his stance at the bottom of
the stairs. Now, in the charged, almost dark silence, three
pairs of eyes watch me. I assume what I hope is a non-
chalant pose as I pull my coat straight and readjust my hat.
In all the rush I had managed to grab my bag, and now
I retrieve the notes. I don't know why the youths had

attacked me or who these men are, but that is not my business, if this is number 14, I must find out if Mrs – I glance down at the notes – Maloney lives here. I clear my throat and ask, 'Does anyone know where I might find Mrs Maloney?'

Eyes look down on me from the darkness, but no one speaks. Light floods the landing above me, and the outline of the men who are sitting in the stairwell stands out in silhouette, a female voice with a Midlands accent calls out, 'Who's down there?'

None of the men speak, so I step forward and, with my foot on the bottom step, I call out, 'It's the nurse, I am looking for Mrs Maloney.'

The silence returns, then, with a click of metal on wood, a shoe with a heel of ridiculous height descends one step, a long thin leg follows, and bending itself almost double over one of the seated men, a body tilts over the stair. I can't see the face, the light is behind it, but I can smell the perfume which is quite overpowering. I repeat my question into the cloud of scent.

'Does Mrs Maloney still live here, please?'

For a moment there is silence, and then the voice asks, 'Who wants to know?'

I reply without hesitation, 'Oh, I'm very sorry, I should have said, I'm the midwife.'

For a moment there is silence, then there is a drone of male voices. One of the men sitting on the stairs half rises, and still in semi-crouched position passes me. Now the voice above speaks quietly, 'You'd better come up.'

7.00 p.m.

The room on the second floor is small, and the air is as redolent inside the room as it is on the stairs. Everything is pink. Rosy curtains hang across the window, which is already heavily shrouded, and the same shade of drape hangs around a double bed. The whole décor is embellished by scatterings of red and pink velvet heart-shaped cushions. Before I have time to take in more of the room, a voice speaks. I had not seen the woman sitting by a small table and I do not really see her now, but I do see the reflection of her face as she looks at me through a mirror which stands over the table. At least I think that it is her face, for a moment I had considered that I was looking at a barn owl, for in the dim light all I can see are pale rings around dark bright eyes.

'Yes,' she repeats.

I realise that I am staring at her, and move my eyes from her reflection as I pull my midwifery bag forward, and step towards her.

'Are you Mrs Maloney?'

She doesn't reply, and continues to look at me through her mirror. Clearing my throat I wade on.

'I'm very sorry to disturb you at this time of night, Mrs Maloney. Mrs O'Reilly, the midwife who has taken over from Mrs Quinn, asked me to call on you. She hasn't seen you at the antenatal clinic for some time, and she wondered if you had moved address.'

She does not speak, and still the round pale rings are directed at me. Filling in the silence I continue.

'Oh, my apologies, I forgot to introduce myself, I am Pupil Midwife Compton.'

I step forward and extend my hand. Still watching me through the mirror she puts down the black pencil she is holding, and starts to rise. She seems very tall, as she wears shoes with heels as high as those of her companion. Her dress moves and the light reflecting from the mirror makes dancing patterns on the wall beside her as she turns. She stands and, leaning backwards towards the mirror, she ignores my extended hand. As yet she has not spoken, and

I am becoming lost to know what to say next. Then, without a word, she pushes past me, her perfume trailing behind her as she snaps on a light. Now the dream world has gone, a rather drab and not very clean room replaces it. She speaks to the wall beside the light switch, her voice cracked with cigarette smoke.

'What do you want?'

Assuming that she is speaking to me, I reply, 'I have called to see if you and your baby are all right.'

Now she swings to face me, and she almost snarls, 'Well, as you can see, we are doing fine.'

Her face is pale, and it almost looks theatrical with its blue eyes and stark red lips, like the face of a clown. I am rather lost for words, so I smile at her, and then, picking up my bag, I try to introduce a light note.

'May I listen to the baby for you while I am here? I'm sure that you would like to know if he or she is OK and still ticking.'

She looks down at the sequined dress which hangs from her shoulders. Little evidence of the small life that rests beneath it shows. Her eyes shine bright, and she screws her face into an unpleasant mask as she throws herself onto the bed and, turning her eyes from me, she looks towards the wall. I can feel the baby, it has risen to just below her umbilicus, and I estimate that she is about six months pregnant, but her dates say that she is seven months. The baby beneath the sequined dress is small, but its heart sounds strong, and I tell her that all is well.

The tall woman, who I now see has hair piled high, comes into the room. She looks across at her colleague, stretches her mouth and raises her shoulders. My patient looks at her and nods her head sideways towards me. I see all of this through the mirror as I busily write down the time of future clinics for Mrs Maloney.

The tall lady precedes me down the stairs, and her shoes

click loudly on each step. Different men now sit on the stairs, and my guardian calls out as we approach them, her voice harsh and penetrating.

'No touching, keep your dirty fingers off, she costs more than any of you could ever dream of owning.'

On my way to Mrs White's house I pass the Burns' house, and Mrs Megs drops the front room curtain back in place as I wave to her. I had gone back to Mrs O'Reilly's to find a note telling me that Mrs White was in labour again. I ride as fast as I can, but baby White is being bathed when I arrive. This time it had not been a false alarm. While Mrs O'Reilly is tending to the baby I tell her all about my visit to Silver Street and she roars with laughter so loud that she nearly frightens the poor baby to death.

I had not heard her laugh before, but now, as we have a cup of tea back at her home and we recall the events of the day, she can hardly stop, and she asks through her laughter, 'Were any of the men left after you announced that you were the midwife?'

I cannot see what the joke is and feel a little offended.

'Some had gone, but there were some more there when I left.'

Wiping tears from her face she gets up from the table as she asks, 'Is she still working?'

I shrug my shoulders, I don't see the joke, and I don't know what she means by work. I had thought that Mrs Maloney was a sad woman, and what was more important is that I had missed a normal delivery by dashing down to see her.

7

Friday 30th March

7.30 a.m.

Without looking at me, Mrs O'Reilly hands me a letter. As usual she is reading her paper. I look at the handwriting on the address. For a moment I don't recognise it and then with some disquiet I tear open the envelope. The letter is from my father, a man of few words spoken and even fewer written; this must be important. Pressing open the single sheet I read:

> *'Dear Dorothy,*
>   *Your mother is ill, please come home.*
>   *Love Father.'*

I turn the page to look for more information, but, true to form, my father has said the minimum possible and the back of the small lined page is blank. I feel Mrs O'Reilly's eyes on me as she lowers her paper to ask, 'Is everything all right?'

I look up and, with a smile that holds no joy, I reply, 'A letter from my father. He says mother is ill and he wants me home.'

She continues to look at me over her paper as she speaks.

'Does your mother suffer from ill health?'

Mother had had pneumonia when I was a child, this

was during the war years, but recently she has been well, thanks to modern medicine and a young newly trained doctor, and I had thought that all would be well. But Father had never been able to manage when mother was ill. He had always seen my role as that of second house-keeper to mother, and we had quarrelled often about my right to have a life of my own. When I was young he had always won. I had left school at the age of sixteen although an academic career in maths was promised. Only mother's support had enabled me to take up a career in nursing, but was mother ill again? Would Father's hold over me pull me back home? Mrs O'Reilly's eyes still rest on me.

'She had pneumonia some years ago and she has a tendency to suffer from respiratory disorders during the winter months.'

The still eyes watch me, and then she speaks, 'Not much on at the moment, I suppose you could take your weekend off starting this afternoon.'

For a moment I am silent. On Wednesday I had seen Tony at the hospital, and as he had said that he would be having a few days off before his final exams we had made a tentative arrangement to spend some time together. I had intended to ask for my weekend then, but now it looks as though my father has won again.

9.00 p.m.

I climb off the bus. My new coat is creased, it hangs crumpled around my legs, and my brown leather shoes feel damp and I am sure that they will have stretched. The bus conductor has carried my leather hold-all on to the pavement, and I thank him as I turn to look at the silent, almost dark village. Light from the public house reflects in the wet pavement, and my past comes back to meet me. The traffic lights turn red, and I walk across the road as the door of The Three Tons public house bursts open. Noise, light, cigarette smoke, and humans are spewed onto the pavement before me, and I step sideways and walk around the stink of beer. No one sees me and I see no one. I know this road well – I have known it all my life. When I was a child we lived in a small miner's cottage just off this road, but now Mother and Father live in a semi-detached house further out of the village. In the post-war years coal miners' remunerations had improved, and Mother, always prudent, had saved for her new home. I knock at the unfamiliar door and, turning the door knob, I push the door open. Mother steps out of a doorway, which, I remember from my last visit, leads into a sitting-room. I can hear a television playing behind her. The hall is dark, and for a moment she peers at me before she asks, 'Is that you, Dorothy?'

I step towards her, and lean forward to kiss her cheek.

'Yes, Mother, it's me.'

For a moment she seems flustered. Her face had felt warm to my touch, but only the warmth of good fire, and not the heat of a fever. Now she regains herself, and calls out as she grasps my bag.

'Good heavens, I didn't know you were coming, why didn't you write and say? I haven't got your bed ready or anything.'

The hall light is now on and I can see my mother. She is shorter than me and a good deal heavier, but she looks well and her eyes behind their glasses have a sparkle to them. For a moment I feel almost angry, but how can I be angry with my hard-working mother? Her whole life has been given to her children.

'Father wrote and said you were ill and that I should come home.'

Mother has returned with a coat hanger, and now I am

relieved of my damp coat and shoes as she bustles me into the kitchen.

'Oh! You know your father, he panics over nothing, I had a bad cough, and the doctor said that I should stay indoors for a time, but it will be spring soon, won't it?'

She asks the question as steam from the kettle mists her glasses. We sit at the table, years fading around us as we drink our cups of tea. My brothers have left home; they are both married and live within the vicinity. My father has hinted several times that I should stop gadding around, and that I should settle down with a sensible man, I am uncertain what sensible means to my father.

10.30 p.m.

The door opens and a draught of cold air enters the sitting room where mother and I now sit. My father, a strongly built man of medium height, enters the room. His face and hair are now quite grey, but his blue eyes still hold the strength and determination of his youth. He had hesitated for some time in the hall, and now speaks as he enters.

'Hmm, didn't think you would get here this quick.'

I stand, walk over to him and kiss his cheek. The cheek feels cold from the outside air and a little sunken. Beer fumes hit me as he turns his face to kiss me, and I am tempted to retort with sarcasm, but the blue, scarred face, and the hard grey hand which touches my cheek, remind me of how much love and consideration I owe this man.

'I can only get one weekend every month, and it was convenient to take this weekend, so I came.'

My voice fades as his eyes stay on my face. He laughs as he speaks.

'I thought it would have to be convenient for you, never mind any bugger else. There you are, Mother, you had better write to your daughter next time and ask her if it will be convenient for you to be ill.'

Now Mother is standing with her hand held to her forehead.

'Can you two stop arguing? You can't be together for one minute before you start.'

I had always known that I favoured my father, not only in looks but also in character; his trait of determination was what pushed me on.

8

Saturday 31st March

9.30 a.m.

At breakfast Mother announces that she does not want me at home with her, that I will only get under her feet and send her mad. One of my sisters-in-law lives in the village; she has been doing my mother's shopping for the last two weeks, and she promises to continue doing so.

2.00 p.m.

I visit several old friends. They are now married and are not at all interested in my world. I take a long silent walk with Father; the green hills of Derbyshire are still beautiful and we call in at a pub where I buy him a pint.

9

Sunday 1st April

11.00 a.m.

I help Mother to cook Sunday lunch and I eat with all the family – my two brothers, their wives and my niece and nephew have visited us.

5.00 p.m.

I climb off the bus in Burnlington and return to my work. I have my mother's blessing, if not my father's. However, the previous day, when we had stopped for a drink at a public house, my father had told a man that I was the clever bugger of the family, and that I now worked in some city somewhere. I always felt that he had a sneaking pride in me. If only I had been a boy.

5.45 p.m.

The light is on in the clinical room. What's happened? Have I missed a delivery? Have I missed several deliveries? I take the stairs two at a time, peeling off my coat as I go. Dropping my bag and coat by the door, I push it a little further open and peer in. Mrs O'Reilly stands with her back to the door, she is wearing her uniform, and her outdoor coat lies on the chair by the door. In my haste I forget my manners and call out, 'Have I missed a delivery?'

She turns her head and looks at me, and then, glancing up at the clock which hangs on the wall over the door, she speaks.

'I didn't expect you back this early, have you had a nice weekend and is your mother well now?'

She turns back to her work and I stand, as I often stand, hesitant in her presence and mumble my reply.

'Yes, Mother is well, it was my father panicking as usual. Have I missed a delivery?'

She turns, and once again looks at the clock.

'If you hurry and get into your uniform, you might be in time.'

6.05 p.m.

I am in the clinical room, my uniform dress is rather crumpled, I had intended to put this one in the laundry before I left on Friday, but now it will have to last for just one more evening. Mrs O'Reilly glances at the dress as I attempt to smooth it out across my body, but she does not speak about it as she turns, with notes held in her hand. Offering me the notes she speaks.

'Mrs Clarke's son rang about ten minutes ago, at least I think that it was him, the poor boy had difficulty in talking on the phone, he said his mother is in labour. You remember Mrs Clarke? She is expecting her eighth so there's not much time for hanging around.'

I have taken the notes from her outstretched hand, but she recovers them before I have time to claim them. Beckoning me over to her side she opens them out on one of the small tables and looks down at them.

'She had quite a heavy post-partum haemorrhage with her last one, and that was only just over a year ago. I've tried to talk her into having this one in hospital, but she won't even think about it.'

For a moment she stands with her lips tightly pressed together and looks at the notes, and then, looking up at my face, she pushes the notes at me and, in a firm voice, gives her order.

'You'd better get a move on if you are going or you will be too late.'

6.25 p.m.

I apply the brakes and drop my feet to the broken pavement edge, the bike comes to a standstill and, after a couple of hops, I gain control of it. I have been to see Mrs Clarke a couple of times already, once with Mrs O'Reilly in her car and once alone on my bike, so I know the house. British Summer Time has arrived, and some of my evening journey has been made by daylight, but there is little light here. Pieces of a factory wall, left standing by Hitler's bombers, loom over me, and this row of houses, which once housed the factory workforce, ends in a pile of rubble. Light, which shows through the few remaining factory windows, gives the end of the road the appearance of a graveyard. Lanky shrubs and last year's weeds make it tawdry. Two pieces of wood stand at right angles to each other and valiantly guard the entrance to the smooth black space which is the front garden of the third house in the row – Mrs Clarke's house.

Diverting my gaze, I push my bike past the abandoned large broken settee which is filled with brown-coloured water and rusty springs. As I raise my hand to knock, the front door is opened by a young man, or maybe I should say an older boy, it is hard to say. In the near darkness of the doorway he looks to be about fourteen or fifteen years of age. He is very tall and almost skeletal. He does not speak, and I have no time to say anything for he claims the handlebars of the bike and, walking backwards, wheels it into the house. I know the room I now enter; it is of fair size, with a broken linoleum floor covering and one large settee which rests against the far wall. There is little comfort within it, and our footsteps sound loud in its cold void. The smell of urine fills the space, and as I look towards the settee I know that several pairs of eyes will be silently watching me through the gloom. Before I have time to approach the children the boy's voice summons me on. The bike has disappeared down what I know to be two concrete steps, and the boy calls from the kitchen.

'Mam's through here, nurse.'

A shuffling noise sounds behind me as I enter the kitchen, and I know that the several pairs of eyes now watch me through the doorway. A gaslight, attached to the wall, throws yellow light across the room; a door stands open at the far side, and a girl dressed in a thin cotton dress and sandals leans on the wall. Two small male figures, which I have just time to see, disappear silently through the door. My bike now leans against a wall in which a door stands closed. I know this door leads to the bedrooms, and I make the assumption that Mrs Clarke has ascended the stairs and now awaits me in her bed. I glance up at the boy, who still holds the handlebars of the bike, as I speak.

'Has your mother gone to bed?'

But it is a woman's voice that answers my question.

'Oh no, nurse, I've just got to get the sandwiches put up for tomorrow, I'll go upstairs in a minute. When you've got a working man in the house you've got to see that he's fed properly.'

I can almost feel the heat radiating from the face of my young accomplice as he supports my bike and, as I peer across towards the window, I see the mother beaming proudly at her eldest son. Turning, she shouts at her eldest daughter.

'Come on, Ruth, get this bread wrapped, I've got to go up with the nurse in a minute.'

Mrs Clarke pushes bread across the wooden table towards the girl, who at about thirteen years of age and is almost as long and thin as her brother. As I recover the gas and air machine and lean it by the door at the foot of the stairs I see Mrs Clarke stop her sandwich making and lean over the table. Stepping towards her, and attempting to use my most authoritative voice, I try to take control of the situation.

'Mrs Clarke, I think it's time that I examined you, can we go upstairs, please?'

Raising her hand to halt my forward movement across the concrete floor, she pulls herself back to standing.

'Just one minute, nurse, and then I'll give you my full attention.'

As she finishes speaking a loud crash sounds behind me and I spin around. A tall, thin man squeezes through the door at the foot of the stairs and, not hesitating, steps over the now prone gas and air machine. Without acknowledging my presence he walks to the table, takes a piece of bread and starts to eat. A badly shaven, dissipated looking face, whose most prominent feature is a red nose, is turned towards me. For a moment he stands tall and straight, a worn jacket hangs from thin shoulders and greying, thick hair rises uncut and uncombed from a large head. But it is a keen eye that considers me, and the face, which he has bequeathed to his son, holds an unquestionable intelligence. He asks, through a shower of crumbs, 'Is it your time?'

No one replies, and with a grunt he steps out of the kitchen and the front door bangs closed. I had been surprised when I had first spoken to Mrs Clarke as she seemed to have a cultured way of speaking which did not relate well to her present situation, and now I have met her husband, he is also somehow ill-fitted to this environment.

7.05 p.m.

I turn and hang my coat behind the kitchen door as I speak and I am now determined to take control of the situation.

'Right, Mrs Clarke, let us go upstairs.'

But I turn to an empty room. The boy stands behind the table polishing off a few remaining crumbs, and as I look around in panic I call out, 'Where is your mother? Where has she gone?'

He looks at me with the large eyes set in a thin face.

'Oh! She's just gone to the toilet nurse, said she had to go before she went upstairs, needed to do a number two.'

He nods his head towards the door leading to the yard. I am out of the kitchen door and blundering across the ill-lit brick-clad yard. Something hits me across the shins, and I fall into a pram. Darkness faces me as I rise, and I have no idea in which direction to run, as I shout out, 'Don't push, Mrs Clarke, do not try to go to the toilet, and don't push.'

The voice sounds beside me and a light appears, my young assistant stands with a candle in a jam jar.

'Are you all right, nurse?'

'Yes, but where is the lavatory? Where is your mother?'

He steps before me as we pass the end of the outhouse. I can hear Mrs Clarke moaning before we reach the toilet door. As I kick the door open the smell of the open lavatory hits me, but the pale face of Mrs Clarke dominates all as she lies prone across the lavatory and cries out, 'Nurse, it's the baby, the baby is here.'

For one moment I am paralysed, then sense, or perhaps training, takes over, and I act.

'Lie still, don't move, don't push, bring some more light please, bring some more light.'

Feet behind me run, and darkness falls. I feel for the baby, its head is not out but I can just feel its smoothness. Mrs Clarke cries out and, trying to control myself, I speak harshly into her face.

'Do not push, take deep breaths, don't push.'

Light, in the form of two candles, appears, along with the boy and the girl. Still speaking towards Mrs Clarke and holding the baby's head, I call to the children.

'Come around here and help me to lift your mother into the yard.'

Light fills the yard outside the lavatory door, and a woman's voice calls out, 'Are you all right out there? Matthew, is everything all right?'

The boy calls out close to my head, and the girl screams outside in the yard, 'Mother's having the baby; she's having the baby in the lav.'

The woman's voice, at first quiet and then loud, calls again, 'Oh my God, Arthur, get out here quick, Mrs Clarke's in trouble.'

The light from the yard is blotted out. A woman's face appears. For a moment it is lit by the candle which the boy holds, and then the candle goes out. Undeterred, the woman blusters forward and, pushing me to one side, she shouts into my ear.

'Move over! Move over! Don't worry, darling, we'll soon have you sorted.'

Mrs Wright is a large lady and the small space in the lavatory has become very crowded, the only place left for the baby and me will soon be in the pan. Lifting the elbow of my arm, which is holding the baby's head, I push its sharp point into the woman's chest and shout into the advancing face.

'I am the midwife. If you could help us to lift Mrs Clarke, I would be much obliged.'

As if stung by a wasp she jumps backwards, and before she lands, she calls out her command, 'Arthur, get out here quick, Mrs Clarke needs you.'

Arthur, in bedroom slippers and braces, is already there, and the situation is taken in hand.

'Tell me how fast you want me to walk, nurse.'

Mrs Clarke is carried in Arthur's strong arms and we reach the kitchen.

'Shall I carry her upstairs, nurse?'

Arthur now stands in the kitchen holding the mother, and I stand and hold the baby's head which has just delivered.

'No thank you Arthur. I think that we had better deliver the baby before we go any further,' I reply.

A thin mat lies beneath my feet, and I kick it straight as I speak.

'Maybe we can lay her on the mat.'

Arthur lowers Mrs Clarke with infinite care as he calls out, 'Matthew, fetch your mother a pillow and a blanket.'

Checking for the cord around the baby's neck I deliver him onto that part of his mother's bare abdomen which shows beneath her dress. A white towel appears across Mrs Clarke's dress almost before the baby lands. I look up at Mrs Wright's plump and serious face as I murmur, 'Thank you.'

Touching her arm to ask forgiveness for my previous rough treatment, I continue, 'Will you please pass over my bag?'

7.25 p.m.

With a lusty cry the baby, a boy, tells his brothers and sisters – who now peer around the various doors – that he has every intention of joining their ranks. I hold him wrapped in a dressing towel and the white bath towel. He makes a fine bundle, but I can see no place to lay him. His mother lies, pale and still, her eyes are closed, and she shows no life or interest in her infant. Then I see Mrs Wright's round face, pale with the exertion and excitement. She focuses on the small bundle. I allow my tone of voice to tell her that she does me a great favour.

'Mrs Wright, would you hold the baby for me, please? I need to see to his mother.' No bundle has been received with more enthusiasm or held with more care.

His mother's hand feels cold and lifeless as she lies pale and still on the concrete floor. The afterbirth has not yet been delivered, and a good quantity of blood now stains the dressing towel which I have placed beneath her. Searching in the bag, I retrieve the ampoule of ergometrine and a syringe, but its introduction into her thigh muscle does little to stem the flow, and the afterbirth remains firmly in situ. I check her pulse, it is not too fast, but it is not very strong.

Rising from my knees, I speak to Arthur.

'Do you think that you could manage to carry her upstairs, Arthur?'

'Certainly, nurse.'

Without hesitation, and with seemingly little problem, he lifts Mrs Clarke and I follow behind as he struggles backwards up the narrow stairs.

7.32 p.m.

I place my hand on Mrs Clarke's abdomen and, finding the top of the uterus, I give it a gentle massage. For a moment it hardens and rises under my hand. I look for the afterbirth but it does not appear. I massage the abdomen again, and this time as it rises I ask the still silent Mrs Clarke to give me a little push. The push produces nothing but more blood, but I am pleased to know that Mrs Clarke can respond to me.

I look at the watch pinned to the gown that I have managed to scramble into. Possibly ten minutes since the baby was born. My mind races to the notes; at the last delivery the placenta had been delayed, then it had taken almost fifteen minutes, but this is one baby later. How long can I wait? My voice sounds loud as I speak.

'Matthew, does your family doctor live near enough for you to run like the wind and fetch him?'

Matthew jumps and starts to turn, but before he has reached the door, Mrs Wright stands up and calls out, 'It's no good going for him, nurse, he doesn't live around here, I don't know where he lives.'

Now I remember, his surgery is held in a bombed-out corner shop, and it is only held three times a week. I had attended an antenatal clinic there two weeks ago. Mrs Wright's sudden movement has made the baby cry and now Mrs Clarke opens her eyes. She looks a little brighter now that she lies in a warm bed, and her daughter has helped remove the damp dress and helped her into a nightdress. Pushing herself up on one elbow, Mrs Clarke asks, 'Is that the baby? What did I have? Is it all right?'

In two seconds Mrs Wright is on her feet, and for so large a lady she makes light work of getting the baby to his mother. Mrs Clarke holds her son and speaks to him for the first time; the baby is pleased to smell the first signs of milk.

'Look at him, wanting food already, he's just like the rest of them.'

She gives a croaking laugh, and with pale trembling hands she gives her son the thin tired breast.

The afterbirth is safely delivered and a little of the bleeding is stemmed.

Mrs Clarke sits in her bed sipping a cup of tea, which Mr Wright has carried in from next door. Children fill the small bedroom, and the new baby is receiving more attention than possibly is good for him. Even the two boys, aged, I would estimate, around six and seven years, have been coaxed into the bedroom by a bag of broken biscuits which Arthur has produced. They watch their new brother from a safe distance while keeping a sharp eye on the biscuit bag. Their names, I gather, are Mark and Luke, and when young John, with his nappy hanging low inside his rubber pants, is pulled onto the bed beside his mother, I realise that the four boys have the names of the disciples.

'So what name will your new brother have?' I ask as I lift him to take him for his bath. Without hesitation, Mrs Clarke replies, 'Peter, I think that should be his name.'

Matthew stands in the doorway and prevents me leaving. His voice is stronger than I had heard before, and it cracks a little as he speaks, he holds a book which I realise is a Bible.

'No, Mother, you know what I feel, Peter denied Christ, it is not a name that I would like for my brother.'

All eyes have turned on the young man. His face changes from white to red, but he stands his ground. 'That's what I think, and you know it.'

Mrs Clarke looks at her son with pride in her eyes, as she asks, 'Then what name shall we give him?'

I had not heard Ruth's voice before, except when she had cried out by the lavatory door. Now, taking the little hand which sticks out from the towelled bundle I hold, she says in a clear voice, 'There was a man who Jesus must have loved, his daddy.'

Her voice catches as the words end and, as tears brim in her eyes, she turns her face away from view. Silence, filled only with the murmur of three baby voices, and the crunch of biscuits, is broken when Mrs Clarke, holding back tears, says, 'Then he shall take Jesus' daddy's name, Joseph it is.'

9.00 p.m.

The small children have been shooed to bed; the teacups have been cleared, and only Mrs Clarke and I remain. The bleeding has not stemmed. In fact it had become worse when Mrs Clarke insisted on climbing out of bed to use the chamber pot, and a large clot of blood had remained after she had climbed back into bed. Now I stand, chamber pot in hand, certain that I must do something, but uncertain what it should be. The doctor is too far away. Should I send Matthew to phone for an ambulance to take Mrs Clarke into hospital? Would she go if I did? She is a forceful woman. Should I send Matthew to ring Mrs O'Reilly? Do we have time to wait for the midwife to come? Mrs Clarke lies pale-faced, her blood pressure has dropped, and the blue rings around her eyes tell me that the ambulance must be sent for.

A loud knock sounds and, as if by magic, Mrs O'Reilly's voice rings out. Her footsteps sound heavy on the stairs and, still holding the chamber pot in my hand, I turn to face her. Without waiting for her words, I speak, and as I hold the evidence in the chamber pot out towards her, I voice my decision.

'I am going to send Matthew to phone for an ambulance.'

Gaining her breath after the stair climb, she speaks. 'Baby all right?'

Pointing the chamber pot towards the broken wicker basket at the bottom of the bed, I reply, 'Yes, it's a boy, and he's fine.'

Without looking at my exhibit she walks to the bed and speaks as she places one hand on the woman's forehead and the other on her wrist.

'Hello Mrs Clarke, how are we doing?'

Without looking at me she speaks as she turns.

'I'll take young Matthew with me; we'll both ring for the ambulance.'

10.30 p.m.

Back home, we sit in the kitchen. Mrs O'Reilly has made poached eggs on toast, I had not realised how hungry I was. Sunday dinner with my family had been my last meal. Mrs Clarke has gone to the local hospital with baby Joseph in tow. She had not complained, she had been too exhausted. The children had all arrived downstairs when the ambulance came; they had not been noisy, but they did get under foot. Matthew and Ruth, ably assisted by Mrs Wright, had been left behind to bring about some control. They had not cried when their mother left. The two boys had stayed together, and the two younger girls, who were named Naomi and Mary, clung tightly to baby John.

'They are a strange family.' I observe almost to myself as I mop up the last of the egg yolk with a piece of toast.

Mrs O'Reilly speaks as she drops into the chair at the other side of the table, 'They are that indeed. Have you read any of the back notes?'

Without waiting for the reply, which is obviously going to be no, she continues.

'I delivered all of her last three. The family have gone downhill very rapidly over the last four or five years. He drinks a great deal you know, and gambles away what money he can't drink. He's got a theory that he can beat the odds at the bookmakers.'

She laughs at this joke, and drinks tea before she continues.

'He's got a degree you know, in maths or something. He used to be a draughtsman, worked at the Morris factory before the war, but he got sent to prison when he refused to join up, said he was a conscientious objector. They lived at a good address before the war, and had just the two children as far as I know. He went away for a long time, went to prison I think; he ended the war in Scotland, slopping out prisoners of war.'

She muses for a moment into her teacup, and I take the opportunity to speak, 'Why was he a conscientious objector?'

Placing her cup firmly in its saucer, she looks across at me.

'You mean you didn't notice? They are very religious; always go to chapel every Sunday. He was a lay preacher before the war, but I don't think he goes to chapel very often now.'

I stand and, lifting my empty plate, I head towards the kitchen sink. She bars my way and places her hand on the arm which carries the plate. Taking the plate from mc, she smiles.

'You made a very good clinical decision there; you did very well, no panic, just a good piece of midwifery.'

Turning, she places the plate in the sink, and it is my turn to blush, such praise, I know, is rare.

'It will be another one that is hard to write up, but we'll manage it.'

10

Monday 2nd April

2.00 p.m.

I follow Mrs O'Reilly through the ward doors. The ward Sister falls in beside Mrs O'Reilly, and I fall even further back; so much authority is not good for a student. Mrs O'Reilly's hand rises in the air and I hear her call, 'Come on, Nurse Compton, catch up with us, this is your case.'

Mrs Clarke sits upright in bed, her white gown fastened tightly to her throat. Pink roses now decorate her cheeks, and her face looks animated as she sees us; the pint of blood that had been transfused into her when she was admitted has done her a world of good. Screens are fetched and placed around Mrs Clarke's bed, and I stand well back as Mrs O'Reilly bends over to speak to her. The ward Sister, in her lace cap, disappears around the screen, and she is quickly replaced by a gentleman who I do not recognise – that is, I don't recognise him until he kisses Mrs Clarke on one of her rosy cheeks. Mr Clarke looks transformed; he still wears the old jacket, but now a white shirt and coloured tie show at his neck, his face is cleanly shaved and his hair is combed and under control. I even think he looks smart as he stands tall and straight. He offers his hand to Mrs O'Reilly, who shakes it cordially and then, turning, he nods to me, and once again the keen eyes surprise me.

A young man with a pale face, dark hair and a white

coat bustles around the screen. He is closely followed by the Sister who slides in behind him. The Sister gathers the notes from the end of the bed, and without remark, steps in front of Mr Clarke. She holds the notes towards the doctor, who, without attention, takes them and looks down at them. The bed sheet is flipped down, and Mrs Clarke's nightgown is pulled up over her abdomen. The doctor places one hand on the abdomen, continues looking at the notes, which he holds in his other hand, and then, without speaking or putting down the notes, he leans over Mrs Clarke, pulls down one of her lower eyelids and grunts.

'I think that your wife is feeling much better, Mr Clarke.'

He makes this announcement to the notes and then, looking up at Mr Clarke, he continues, 'It was a close call last night; your wife could have bled to death.'

After this proclamation he smiles, looks down at the notes, turns a page and then looks up again.

'I think that it would be inadvisable for your wife to carry another pregnancy, and we suggest that her fallopian tubes be ligatured to prevent such an occurrence.'

He stops speaking, looks from Mr Clarke to Mrs Clarke, smiles, says, 'Think it over,' and turns.

Passing between the screens with Sister, who leaves in tandem with him, he mumbles to her, 'We could get her on the list tomorrow morning, can't keep the bed blocked with a community cock-up.'

Mrs Clarke's cheeks are redder than they were before. Mr Clarke looks at the half-closed screen, and for the first time I see emotion in his face, it is the emotion of anger. He looks like a man who would like to box someone's ears. Mrs O'Reilly has headed for the side of the bed, but before she can speak Mr Clarke has placed his arm around his wife's shoulders, and has pulled her to him. 'Come on,

May, come on, don't get upset, it's your health we've got to think about, we've got a big enough family now.'

Mrs O'Reilly and I slide away between the screens.

11

Tuesday 10th April

10.00 a.m.

I sit in Mrs O'Reilly's sitting-room with my Case Book open in front of me. I have spent an hour in the clinical room completing the midwifery notes and entering details into my own case notes. Mrs O'Reilly had said that I should sit in the warm room to write the cases into my Case Book. Tomorrow I must go back to the hospital and present it to my tutor.

One month of the three-month course has passed and I have four completed cases recorded. I am only just on track with the examination schedule.

Number one, Mrs Burns: I had finalised this case a few days ago, no problems. Number two, Mrs Wardle: I had been to see her on her first day but no one had answered the door. What had happened? Had Mrs Wardle bled to death? I was there at nine-thirty, I should have been there at seven, or even six-thirty. I had got into a bit of a panic, and was just starting to run around in circles when the door across the landing had opened. Mrs Hall had stayed with Mrs Wardle all night, and at seven-thirty a man and woman had arrived in a car and had taken her away. Mrs Hall had not asked who they were or where they lived. I had been more than pleased when, two days later, I had found Mrs Wardle back in the room with her chil-dren. Mr Wardle was out looking for more suitable accommodation, and I had been pleased that he did not find it before the ten days lying-in period was over. Now all I have to do is convince my tutor that I did not lose the continuity of care during the two days that mother and baby had disappeared. Number three, Mrs Murphy: apart from some unexplained lapses of time, which will have to be accounted for, the case had been straightforward. Number four, Mrs West: Baby James had a rash on his bottom which I had felt had been caused by his mother's anxiety. He is a hungry baby and nothing is denied him. I have handed him and his mother over to the health visitor.

Four cases completed, rather a low score and a lot of explaining to do. Never mind, as Mrs O'Reilly had said, 'This is midwifery in the real world, not in a textbook.'

Wednesday 11th April

2.00 p.m.

The class has gathered. Maureen is not here, someone says that she has been ill with a very bad cold and has been ordered to bed. I ask myself if I should go round to see her. The answer comes quickly, 'No, you'll catch her cold and then you'll never get your twelve cases recorded.'

2.30 p.m.

I sit in my tutor's office; she has been reading my Case Book for some time. She looks up at me over her glasses and, as she speaks, her voice is stern.

'There seem to be some strange time lapses in the recordings of your deliveries, Nurse Compton. Do you have recordings other than the ones here in your Case Book?'

I draw in a deep breath, long explanations whirl in my head and I'm not sure how I am going to deal with them. But she does not give me time as, with voice a little modified, she continues, 'How are you dealing with the city centre area? I understand that your midwife has had to take on the responsibility for an umm, umm, rather difficult patch. Have you had dealings with any of these cases?'

I draw in breath again, but I have no time to speak as Miss Perkins continues, 'I was unsure about you staying there, but you seem to be getting your cases. Now, if you have any problems that you cannot handle, or if you find yourself being put in untenable situations, don't hesitate to call me, or even come into the school.'

Giving me her most benevolent smile, she pushes my Case Book across her desk. Mumbling that I will not think twice about contacting her, I retrieve my book and leave her office.

4.00 p.m.

In the Students Union coffee bar I sit with a couple of the other girls and chew over life's problems. Tony had phoned last night to say that he might be having coffee around this time and, if he didn't have to go onto the wards, we could meet. I look around the crowded, untidy room. I won't be able to wait long, but I don't want to miss him. Now I see him coming in with some of his fellow students. He waves to me but continues on and sits with them. One of the girls who I am with stands and, gathering up her bag, mumbles, 'I must go; I've got a case due this evening.'

The girl sitting beside me also rises.

'Yes I must go too; I can't afford to miss a case.'

I call out to her back as she heads for the door, 'See you next week.'

I stand and fasten up my raincoat and as we disperse I glance towards a table which is surrounded by young men in short white coats. I see Tony's hand rise and wave me over. He leans back on two legs of his chair as he calls, 'Sorry I was late, busy ward round. Listen, before you go, we're having a party at a senior house officer's flat a week on Saturday, do you think that you will be able to come? It will start around seven.'

Several of the young men start to rise and, pushing his chair back, Tony rises above me. He pushes his dark hair out of his eyes and looks down at me with clear brown eyes. I will make every effort to be at the party.

'I will have to ask my midwife about the off duty. Can I ring you this weekend?'

My voice fades as, skipping sideways to catch up with his colleagues, he throws me a kiss and is gone.

5.30 p.m.

The smell of food hits me as I open the door. I had not realised how hungry I am. The drama with my tutor has quite exhausted me. Mrs Stone is coming down the stairs.

'Just in time again, good job I made enough food for two of you.'

I smile at her as we squeeze past each other. The tutor's words ring in my ears, I had no idea what she was talking about, but from now on I intend to carry out textbook deliveries. I do not wish to be moved as I have no intention of missing out on the delicious stews that arrive at regular intervals in the upstairs kitchen.

We sit at the table, our plates steaming, and Mrs O'Reilly looks across at me through clouded glasses as she asks, 'Did you see your tutor?'

I nod yes as a piece of hot potato burns my tongue.

'What did she have to say?'

Mrs O'Reilly removes her glasses and wipes steam from them; she is very short-sighted without her glasses so I know that I will be able to be a little economical with the truth if I hurry and get the words out before she can replace her spectacles. So, looking straight at her, I say, 'She didn't say much at all, just told me to take more care with my recording.'

I can feel my face burning and, as she puts on her glasses, I look down at my hot food. She looks hard at me.

'That doesn't sound like a hospital tutor to me, did she say anything about the number of cases you have?'

She stows food in her mouth as she finishes speaking and I take my time in replying as I choose my words carefully.

'She said she knows that this is a difficult area.

I see her pupils dilate behind their thick lenses and I quickly add to my words, 'At least she said that she knows that Mrs Quinn's area, which we have taken on, is a difficult one.'

I had not fully understood what the tutor had meant by her comments, but Mrs O'Reilly does.

'That sounds more like it, I thought that they would start moaning about normal midwifery. I wonder how they think babies are born in some of these areas. They think if there isn't a father standing to attention at the end of the bed the baby will come out in a different way.'

She stows food in her mouth and, chewing rapidly, gets ready for the next onslaught. I am saved by the bell.

6.30 p.m.

The Wainwright family lives on the road which runs parallel to the one where Mrs O'Reilly lives and it takes me only a little time to get to it. Mrs Wainwright herself answers the door and she invites me into the house. Asking if I might bring in my bike, I follow her in. We are in a hall, similar to the one which runs across the ground floor of Mrs O'Reilly's house and I feel quite at home as I follow the lady through to the kitchen. She is a woman of medium height, I should say a good three inches taller than me, but the thing that strikes me about her is her face, she is very beautiful, and I have to take a second look to make sure I have seen her correctly the first time. Her hair is very dark and, even in this late stage of pregnancy, she looks elegant with it piled high on her head and kept in place by silver pins. The long loose maternity dress, with its sailor's collar, hangs long behind her but rises some inches at the front to reveal pink satin slippers that click as she walks before me along the hall. A small boy, with hair as dark as his mother's, sits on a mat in front of a guarded fire. He rises and hides behind his mother's skirt. I have carried my bag with me but have left the gas and air machine with the bike, and I wait for her to settle the child before I ask, 'Are you having contractions, Mrs Wainwright?'

She smiles across at me, her hand still resting on her son's head.

'I was, nurse, but as soon as we got back from the phone they seemed to stop.'

I look around the well-furnished, clean room, as I ask, 'Are you on your own?'

Her cheeks blush as she replies, 'My husband is usually home by this time, but sometimes he has to work late.' A contraction arrives, and she leans against the table until it passes.

'Do you think that we could go to the bedroom, and I can then examine you and see how you are doing?'

The bedroom is cold as the three of us enter. The bay window overlooks the garden and, having drawn the curtain and switched on the electric light, Mrs Wainwright returns to the bed. I know this room, I have seen it before, I know that the flowered carpet is swept and unmarked, I know that the doilies on the dressing table match the cover on the bed, and that both match her pink slippers and her dressing-gown. I know that the room will be agreeable, it holds everything you need, but I also feel that something is missing; the something that denotes the fondness of and appreciation for the small things that hold love. The doilies on the dressing-table look different to those which adorn Mrs Burns' broken furniture, maybe the last touch of pleasure and endearment has not been delivered to them, as it has been to the worn and darkened ones. I examine her. Her son watches me closely from his vantage point above her head. Labour has started, but things have not progressed very far. Placing her notes on the dressing table, I carefully record my findings; this is going to be a 'textbook' delivery, all recordings exact.

'Should I light the fire, nurse? I know that the baby will want some warmth.' She is struggling to stand as the small boy adds to her problem by hanging onto her neck. A coal fire has been laid in the large ornate fireplace. This room had once been a sitting room and the fire basket is large. The coals in its centre look few and the room feels chill and somehow unresponsive. I hesitate for a moment.

'Your labour has only just started, Mrs Wainwright; it could be a few hours before the baby is born.' I look around the large room; with its high ceiling and small modern furnishing, it will take some heating. 'But maybe we should start warming the room now.'

7.20 p.m.

The table has been cleared and my half-eaten stew has disappeared. A note on the table tells me that Mrs O'Reilly will be out until about eight thirty, but there is no mention of what has happened to my stew. The kitchen is warm, and it takes little time to find my meal – rather dry but warm – in the bottom of the oven.

Mrs O'Reilly pokes her head around the sitting-room door and her voice makes me jump as I sit with my feet resting on her footstool.

'Has Mrs Wainwright delivered? That was quick.'

Dropping my feet from the stool, I stand as I explain the situation. Throwing her coat over the back of a chair, she asks, 'Is she still on her own?'

'She said that her husband would soon be home.'

I am now standing and ready to run; not another case gone astray, I hope. She continues speaking, her voice unbending, 'I asked you if she was on her own, the answer I think is that you do not know.'

The telephone rings, and I escape. Mrs Wainwright sounds quite anxious now, and I call out as I fall down the stairs pulling on my coat as I go.

'I'm going back to see her now.'

8.30 p.m.

The smell of smoke greets me as she opens the door, and as we enter the bedroom, billows of smoke leave the fireplace and fill the room. Slamming the window shut we all retreat to the kitchen. After a few minutes we return to the bedroom. The fire has stopped smoking but the labour has progressed little.

Back in the kitchen we sit and drink tea. There is nothing else that I can do, I will have to sit with Mrs Wainwright and wait.

Robert has been put to bed. His cot has been carried into the kitchen and it has taken half an hour of sitting in darkness to get him to sleep.

The front door opens, and feet sound on the hall tiles, the door had opened earlier when the man who lives upstairs came home, but this time Mrs Wainwright jumps to her feet as she recognises the footstep. I hear his voice as he almost falls over my bike, and the door opens to admit a handsome, strongly built man in his early thirties. Not taking his eyes off me, he removes his overcoat, leans over his wife, places his hand on her abdomen, and kisses her face. With red cheeks she kisses him back as she murmurs, 'Darling, this is the midwife, I had to phone her.'

Walking past me he hangs his coat on a hanger behind the door and, turning, he looks at me again, 'Are you the regular midwife?'

Without waiting for an answer, he continues, 'I must say you are an improvement on the old witch who came a few weeks ago; if you are going to come regularly I think that we might have a few more nippers.'

He is looking down at me as I sit by the table. His eyes twinkle and a provocative smile hangs on his lips. I am lost for words. Gathering my wits, I rise and extend my hand.

'I presume you are Mr Wainwright, I am pleased to see you. I think your wife is in need of your help.'

Taking my hand, he holds it in his and, with mirth filling his voice, he says, 'Such a pretty little hand, you must take care of it, and stop soaking it in so much water.'

His wife has poured him a cup of tea and, taking it from her, he helps her lower herself into a chair as a contraction rises.

'So you need some more help do you, darling? I don't know, you women are always needing help.'

Standing by her, he places his hand on her abdomen and kisses her forehead. The child stirs in the cot; kissing two fingers he presses them on the child's head.

He has taken over, all is under his control, and with a languid voice he dismisses me.

'I'll give you a ring when the baby is ready to come, nurse. I'm loath to part with such a pearl, but duty calls.'

Again his smile is teasing, and his eyes twinkle as he pushes me and my bike out of the front door.

9.45 p.m.

I open the sitting-room door; Mrs O'Reilly looks at me over the back of her chair, 'She had it then?'

'No she hasn't, but her husband is home, and he seems to have everything under control.'

She snorts a laugh down her nose as she turns back to the television.

'So you met him, did you? Quite a character, isn't he? Marry some strange men do some women.'

I can feel my face blush as I walk around and sit in the other armchair. She looks at me and laughs.

'Been giving you the chat has he? He's an actor at the Repertory Theatre you know. I don't think he knows if he's on the stage or off it half the time. Take no notice of him.'

I smile; I don't want to tell her what he called her, not that I think she would care, she would probably just laugh.

10.30 p.m.

I am in the sitting room. Mrs O'Reilly has retired; she said that I must decide what I should do. Mrs Wainwright could be in labour for hours yet but I'm not sure if it is worth going to bed. I sit half-asleep in the warm room. The phone rings.

'Is that the pretty little nurse? If it is then my wife will be giving birth at any moment, if it isn't she, then tell her to get out of bed at once.'

The line goes dead. I look at my watch, less than an hour since I left Mrs Wainwright, she has certainly moved along pretty quickly if she is giving birth, but there is nothing to do but go and see.

When I arrive at the house the door opens and Mr Wainwright, dressed in a velvet dressing-gown, lets me in.

'In time, and as beautiful as ever, eh, nurse.'

He waves me into the bedroom where the fire burns bright. Mrs Wainwright lies in bed, labour is obviously well advanced, and I hurriedly give her the gas and air machine.

11.00 p.m.

Mrs Wainwright gives birth to a baby boy, a normal delivery with no complications, except, once again, there appear to be some time discrepancies. I had examined my patient at 6.30 p.m., at which time labour had only just begun. I had seen her again at 8.30 p.m. I had done an internal examination and labour had not advanced far. Now, at 10.30 p.m., with no further intervention on my part, she is giving birth.

11.15 p.m.

'You have a fine son, Mr Wainwright.'

I speak to him as he watches me bathe his son. I feel a little embarrassed by his nearness and try to retain control by speaking in a professional manner.

'Your wife's labour progressed quite quickly; it had been rather slow in its early stages.'

Leaning over and touching his son's head he speaks into my ear, his voice intimate.

'Well she did ask me for some help, and how can a man help his wife to overcome such stress? Love is all, nurse, love is all.'

I look sideways at his randy face, which is still close to mine.

'There is much that is not written in books, nurse, you will enjoy the learning I am sure, and I envy the man who teaches you.'

I look at the case notes, what on earth can I write? Only that which I know happened can be written in the appropriate spaces, and once again the times do not add up.

12

Thursday 12th April

2.00 p.m.

The weather has brightened up somewhat, and for the first time since I started cycling around these streets I feel that I can sit upright and do not have to defend myself against the elements. I am in Mrs Quinn's area looking for 46 Canal Street, where I must visit a woman who Mrs Quinn saw some weeks ago but who has not been seen by Mrs O'Reilly or me. On the map a canal had been shown, and the street I look for had joined the street I am now on, to this canal. Few street names remain to guide me, in fact few streets have endured, just pavements covered with red brick dust. Houses without fronts or roofs show that streets with names were once here. Few buildings have been left standing in this part of the city. Mrs O'Reilly had said that they had taken a beating from the bombers when Hitler was trying to destroy the canal. I have ridden down a couple of these ravaged streets and each ended in a pile of rubble. The bombers had certainly done a good job. Shrubby trees peer through garlands of detritus and no sign of the canal remains. Moving slowly through this uninhabited desolation I meet no one. Then, marvel upon marvel, a corner shop comes into view; it takes more than bombs to destroy British commerce. An elderly man stands in its doorway. He is looking down at his hand and his lips move in silent speech. I call out as I swing my bike across the street.

'Excuse me, can you tell me where Canal Street is?'

I drop my feet to the ground and stand before him. He looks up from the hand which holds money, and stares at my face. His grey, lined face remains immobile, he does not speak, and a voice addresses me from behind him as a large lady in apron and headscarf pushes him to one side.

'It's right at the end of this road hen, just keep riding, you can't miss it.'

She waves a plump arm in the direction that I am already travelling, smiles a stiff smile, turns and, with waddling gait, sets off up the road. The man has not moved, nor has his gaze left me. I mumble my thanks to the woman and turn back to the man. His colourless eyes look into mine, but they seem not to see, no spark of human recognition shows. The scar starts on his forehead and widening, disappears upwards taking most of his hair with it. For a moment I look at the scar and then I realise that the man is not as old as I had at first thought him to be. The side of the face that remains unscarred is that of a man in his early thirties. Fumbling for his pocket he reveals air force blue trousers. Clouds block out the few rays of sun and wind blows paper and rubbish along the pavement, piling some of it against his legs. Mumbling goodbye, I peddle away. I look back, the man does not move and the world fit for heroes continues to ignore him.

Just before West Street joins a busy road I find Canal Street on my right. There are few numbers on doors and Canal Street is longer than the other streets that I had explored. At last I find number 46. It lies at the corner of the street. I say it lies at the corner of the street because part of the premises lies on Canal Street and part lies on Well Street, it is a corner shop. That is, it used to be a corner shop, now the shop window, which overlooks

Canal Street, is papered over with newspaper and the shop door is obviously not in use as rubbish fills it. Wheeling my bike down Well Street, I seek another entrance. A high gate hangs off its hinges and reveals a passageway which runs between the back buildings of the shop and the house that stands next to it.

2.20 p.m.

I congratulate myself on finding number 46 and, pushing the gate a little further open, I wheel my bike through it. The blue brick yard is clean; no rubbish gathers here. A clothes line, which stretches between the wall of the house and the back of the shop, supports freshly washed clothes. A heavy brown door, with peeling paint, stands ajar. I wheel my bike past the door and, leaning it against the wall, return to the door. The sound of my knock does not seem to travel far and no one answers it. I peer around the door; another door lies a few feet further into the building, so stepping cautiously into the space between the doors I knock on the second door. A voice, which I assume to be a woman's, calls out loud and clear.

'Hello, who is there?'

Thankful that I have found someone at home, I reply, 'Good afternoon, I am the midwife, I have called to see Mrs Ramshaw if she is at home. Mrs Quinn is unable to visit . . .'

My explanation is cut short as the voice calls out again, 'Missus not in, gone shopping.'

I stop to think for a minute, maybe I should wait for her to return. I will ask the lady if she knows when Mrs Ramshaw will return. I start to speak, but the voice interrupts me again as it calls out, 'Come in, do come in, come in now.'

Mumbling my thanks and collecting my bag I step

through the door. I enter a long thin room, which is lined on either side with a variety of chairs. A narrow, well-worn carpet runs from just inside the door, through which I have just entered, and continues up to a closed door in a wall at the far end of the room. Although there is no other furniture except a small table which stands in the middle of the room, the room feels quite comfortable. I stand, feeling a little at a loss; there is no sign of the woman to whom I have been talking. Making a coughing sound to alert the woman to the fact that I am standing in her house, I ask, 'Do you think that Mrs Ramshaw will be long?'

'Sit down, sit down and make yourself comfortable.'

The commanding voice sounds from behind a door which stands ajar in the corner of the room. The lady must be in the kitchen I assure myself and, taking out Mrs Ramshaw's notes, I look at them. She had only moved here a couple of weeks before Mrs Quinn went on maternity leave. There is little recorded on the notes, and certainly little about her accommodation, or of the relatives with whom she might be living.

The silence is absolute, no sounds of domestic activity come from the direction of the kitchen, and to reassure myself that the lady is still there, I speak, 'Much better weather today, isn't it?'

Before I have time to develop the theme, the voice interrupts me.

'Much better weather, much better weather, has been some bad weather, oh yes, bad weather.'

I try to continue the conversation in the hope that the lady will make her presence known.

'Maybe spring is here.'

'Oh yes, spring is here, spring is here.'

As the voice rings out, the door to the outside world opens, and a pushchair and a young woman come through it. I jump to my feet as the voice from the kitchen calls, 'Oh yes, spring, come in, do come in.'

The young woman looks at me as I point towards the kitchen door.

'Your mother, or some lady, invited me in . . .'

My explanation goes no further, letting go of the push-chair, and with lips drawn back and eyes like slits, the young woman heads towards the kitchen door, shouting as she goes.

'That sod, I'll kill it one of these days, just you see if I don't.'

For a moment I am taken aback, then, feeling aghast, I leap to my feet and follow her. Is she going to attack some elderly relative who has done nothing more than invite me into her home? The room is dark but a high window throws light onto a contraption at the far end of the room. It takes some time for me to recognise what I am seeing, and the commotion, which now erupts, gives me little guidance. Now I see that in the far side of the room there is an enormous wire cage which extends across the wall, and a dead tree branch stretches from one end of this cage to the other. A good-sized black bird hops from one part of the branch to another and, between squawks, in a deep voice it shouts profanities, familiar only to the male population of the Teeside docks. At the same time the young woman beats the cage and offers several profanities of her own. The bird jumps from one part of the branch to another and continues to insult her, changing its voice several times as it does so. Satisfied that she had told the bird what she thinks of it, the young woman turns her back on it.

Feeling totally nonplussed, I follow the young woman back into the outer room; had I been holding a con-versation with a mynah bird? The young woman does not speak to me, she reclaims the pushchair, and sets off across the room with it. This is definitely not a good start. Should I go back out onto the yard and start again? As my bag falls to the floor, the bird calls out again. I certainly don't want to start another conversation, so I grab the bag and hasten after the young woman feeling rather like Alice chasing the white rabbit. She opens a door at the far end of the room and now I definitely feel that I am following her into the rabbit burrow. The room is light, but it is a strange diffused light, not dark and not light, sort of a pale grey, like the light on a misty morning. Then I realise I am looking at the newspaper on the inside of the shop window; I am in the shop. The young woman crosses the shop, passing a double bed, a dressing table of sorts, a rack containing clothes, and a chair. Without looking back at me she lifts part of what I assume to be the shop counter, and passes through into the front of the shop. She returns with a large shopping bag and, still ignoring me, she starts to unload tins of food and loaves of bread onto the shelves on the inner side of the counter. I am unsure as to whether I have entered some new dimension in which I am invisible, therefore to test things out I cough in my hand and then try speaking.

'Mrs Ramshaw? Erm, I am looking for Mrs Ramshaw.'

She rises from her shelf-stacking, and heads back through the gap. A small child appears above the counter, it hangs there for a few moments, its eyes resting on me and then it disappears. The silence continues. The sound of a car engine passes. Then, as her body appears above the counter, without looking at me, she speaks, 'I've been looking for you for the last couple of weeks, nobody seems to know where you hang out.'

Clearing my throat, I start my explanation and excuses, but she interrupts me, 'This wouldn't happen on Merseyside you know, we know how to look after each other there. But that bugger had to come down here to look for work.'

She nods her head sideways as she speaks, and I look in the direction in which she nods, but there is no one there. I attempt another apology.

'I am very sorry.'

I get no further as, passing back through the opening once again, she peels off a coat and, pushing her distended abdomen towards me, she continues in a quiet but determined voice, 'I suppose you want to have a look at this – believe me it's alive and kicking.'

I assure her that I will check the baby, but first I need some details for the notes. Sinking into the only chair in the shop she looks across at me, I stand above her with notes in my hand, and nodding her head forwards she speaks. 'Sit on the bed if you want to, nurse.'

I lower myself onto the side of the bed and, swinging my bag sideways, I drop it behind me.

The movement is sudden, and I leap to my feet. The far side of the bed starts to move, and a tousled head of black hair appears above the blankets. Dark round eyes look at me from a long thin brown face, and the woman behind me laughs.

'Oh! He's on nights, might have known he'd wake up as soon as anybody came in, got a nose as long as an elephant he has.'

I look at the man in amazement, no wonder he woke up, I had dropped my bag on his legs. I start to mumble my apologies and to move towards the door, but in one silent action he slides his long, thin, naked body out of the bed and into a pair of trousers. Without speaking or looking at me, he passes around the end of the bed and, grabbing a shirt from the rack of clothes, he is gone.

3.00 p.m.

I wheel my bike out onto the street. The baby is fine, all is well and the confinement should take place within the next four weeks. I have entered a few details in the notes. The father is of West Indian origin, he lives with the mother, and is the father of both her children. The mother's sister, who I did not meet, lives in one of the upstairs rooms, and she will be with Mrs Ramshaw when the baby is born. The mynah bird had shouted goodbye to me as I passed through the outer room, and it was with some difficulty that I had refrained from answering. Now, as I peddle back up West Street, I have the distinct feeling that I have just left Wonderland.

13

Friday 13th April

10.00 a.m.

We have sorted out the off duty; it was quite a complicated thing to do as Mrs O'Reilly must have her off duty when another midwife can take over her district. I am included in the district and only one of the midwives in the neighbouring districts was willing to take responsibility for me. We had the discussion yesterday evening when I returned from Wonderland, and with all the phone calls, and the visit from Miss Grey, who proved to be as colourful as her name, I began to think that I had brought Wonderland back with me along with half its characters. However, I now sit curled up in my bed with textbooks open in front of me. I am to have today off and am on duty over the weekend. I will be under the guidance of Miss Wilkins as Mrs O'Reilly is having the weekend off and she is going away to a conference. But most important of all I have next Saturday evening off, I can go to the party. I rang Tony last night, and now I sit with a warm glowing feeling inside me. Concentrating on exams is hard.

14

Saturday 14th April

2.30 p.m.

The textbooks are still open but I find reading hard. I have looked at the notes of women who might deliver in the next couple of days. There are only two; they both live nearby and neither should present a problem. I have packed all the delivery bags, that is, three in all, and both gas and air machines are full and working. There is not much else that I can do. I have checked with Mrs Stone at least three times to make sure that she knows all the procedures and numbers for contacting Miss Wilkins. She is very tolerant of my insecurity and has diligently gone through the numbers with me on each occasion. Nothing more to do but sit and wait. I would try to visit both the ladies this afternoon just to reassure myself, but Mrs O'Reilly had said that I must not go wandering off meaninglessly as I might miss a phone call. The ring of the phone makes me jump out of my skin, and with heart beating fast I leap to the door eager to hear which of the ladies has gone into labour first.

'Hello, Mrs O'Reilly's house, Pupil Midwife Compton speaking, may I help you?'

For a moment there is silence, and then a man's voice asks, 'That the lady midwife's house?'

The voice is not one that I had expected. I know both of the women who are due and I have met their husbands.

Pulling myself together I reply, 'Yes this is the midwife's house, this is Pupil Midwife Compton speaking, how may I help you?'

I hear the large intake of breath and I can hear other voices mumbling in the background.

'Oh I am very pleased to find you, Pupil Midwife Compton. My wife, I think that soon she will have the bambino, she has many cramps and much pain.'

Now the voice fades somewhat and I can hear several voices all talking in an agitated manner. Now I hear the man's voice again, but it is not talking to me, it is talking to someone else who is by the phone and I cannot understand a word that is being said. The voices rise to a crescendo and the man's voice returns. This time he is talking to me, and he is speaking English.

'Pupil Midwife Compton, will you please come to my house to see my wife, Mrs Macaronis.'

Grabbing the pencil which hangs by the note pad, I shout into the phone, 'Yes, Mr Macaronis, I will come, but what is your address.'

A hubbub of voices fills the line as I shout, 'Mr Macaronis, Mr Macaronis, what is your address?'

The voice returns through a background of noise.

'My address is 1172 Burlington Road, it is on the way into town, it is the large Italian Restaurant which stands across the road from the fire station. I wait for you by the shop, OK?'

The voice calls out in what I now presume to be Italian, and the line goes dead.

For a moment I stare at the phone, Mrs Macaronis, for the life of me I can't think who she is. I am sure that I have not seen her and 1172 sounds a long way down Burlington Road. The shop must be almost in the city, a part of Mrs Quinn's area. Falling down the stairs, I frantically try to recall the case. I find the notes in the drawer containing

Mrs Quinn's case notes and as I read them I remember that I had tried to make a visit last week, but finding nobody at home and the restaurant closed, I had recorded, 'No one at home.' I had intended to pay another visit next week as the expected date of delivery was not for another three weeks. I groan inwardly, I am going to ride almost into town along the busy main road on Saturday afternoon, only to find that labour has not yet started. I check the notes, it is a first baby, no doubt the head has just gone down. I moan to myself as I fasten my coat and pick up the equipment.

2.45 p.m.

It takes ages to cross the main road, I walk back along the pavement to the traffic lights and cross when they change. The flow of traffic is heavy, lots of lucky people going into town, to the shops no doubt. It had rained earlier, and as I ride in gutters full of every kind of wet rubbish I receive several unwelcome showers. The even numbers are on the other side of Burlington Road and as I pass the fire station I drop my feet to the ground and look across the road. A man in shirt sleeves stands at the pavement edge. A short distance down the road the traffic lights change and when the traffic on my side slows down I make a dash for it – well as much of a dash as I can with all the kit on board! The man sees me and, leaping across the road, he grabs the handlebars of the bike and propels it forward with speed. Oncoming cars head for us and the man, waving his free arm around over his head, offers curses to their drivers in tones that I am sure the Pope would not have approved of.

I am cold, wet and not in good humour as I follow the man and my bike down a narrow poorly lit passage. There is a strong smell of food, and I assume that we are walking down the side of the restaurant. A door at the end of the passageway opens, and I am pushed through it. Heat, light, sound and, above all, the smell of food, meet me, and for a moment I think that we must be in the restaurant. I try to return to my bike which has been left in the passageway, but the door has closed. A man and woman stand beside me with wine glasses in their hands, they are elegantly dressed and the woman's perfume is heady as she turns from me. I am lost and out of place, I have been directed to the wrong place, no one is speaking in English, I must find my way out of here. A hand takes my elbow and I am halted. An elderly lady with silver-grey hair and genteel dress stands beside me. Speaking quietly in what I assume to be Italian, she takes my arm and leads me forward. Dark eyes are raised towards us and, excusing herself, a young woman with jet black hair and a beautiful smiling face leaves a group and steps towards us. She smiles at me, but listens to the elderly lady. She speaks first in Italian before speaking to me in English.

'My mother greets you and welcomes you to our house. She says that you are too young and too beautiful to work as a midwife, but she is sure that you will bring her a grandson. May I take your coat?'

I unbutton my raincoat, the young woman divests me, and I stand in a warm well-lit room. With its lavish drapes and festive atmosphere I am sure that I have entered by the wrong door, I am sure that I am in a party. I smile at the young woman, who still stands before me, and ask, 'Is Mrs Macaronis here? A gentleman rang me to say that she is in labour, I hope that I am not . . .'

But my uncertainty is brought to an end, and calling out loud and clear as he crosses the room, a well-built man in his middle years bears down on me.

'Pupil Midwife Compton, how pleased I am to see you.'

Putting his arm through mine he propels me forward across the room; faces smile at me, couples move out of the way as we pass, and a door in an adjacent wall is opened before we reach it.

'My wife is waiting for you.'

He speaks as he propels me through the door and into a large annexed room. This room is furnished as lavishly as the one I have just left, and it is again peopled. I hear the shout and then see the large bed on which a woman lies, I see her hands grasp and pull on its wooden, carved, upright, posts as two women descend on her. I hear voices call out behind me, and the two women step back from the bed. The older one crosses herself as she walks backwards past me. I feel quite alarmed, but now I know that I am in the right place; whatever is happening in the other room is not my business, this is.

The gas and air machine is carried in by Mr Macaronis and my bag follows in the hands of the young woman with the beautiful hair. The crescendo of sound rises as the door opens; I am surprised and ask Mr Macaronis, 'Could you ask the people in the other room if they would mind being a little quieter, I am sure that your wife would like a little rest between her contractions.'

He looks at me with wide eyes as he speaks, 'Is my wife going to have my son now?'

I intend to say that she might give birth to his daughter, but he has gone and, grasping his wife to him, he rains her face with kisses as he speaks to her. Rising, he turns towards the door and as he passes me he wipes tears from his face.

'You may stay with your wife if you wish to, Mr Macaronis, it will be quite all right.'

He looks at me and a shudder seems to run through his body. 'Oh no, nurse, this is woman's work, we men can but wait and marvel.'

He is gone but as the door opens and closes behind him there is silence, he had not left and asked for quiet, but as I look around the room I realise that an older lady had.

3.30 p.m.

I have examined Mrs Macaronis, labour is well established and all seems to be going well. I look at her notes; I have had little time to peruse them properly before this moment. Mrs O'Reilly and I had looked at them and had discussed the case, but as the baby was not due to be born for another three weeks and as I had not managed to find Mrs Macaronis at home on my previous visit, I had not put the case to mind. Now I turn the pages and, as with many of Mrs Quinn's cases, there is scant detail to read, but I do read, with some alarm, that Mrs Macaronis is thirty seven years of age and this is her first pregnancy. There are few details recorded on the pregnancy. I speak to the young woman who has stayed with Mrs Macaronis. Mrs Macaronis herself is working hard with the gas and air machine.

'Do you know if Mrs Macaronis visited her doctor during her pregnancy?'

Without letting go of the hand which holds the mask the woman leans sideways, opens a drawer on a bedside table and passes me a blue card. Giving me a fleeting smile, the woman returns her attention to Mrs Macaronis, who I now know to be her sister. Good, Mrs Macaronis has attended her doctor's clinic quite regularly. The pregnancy had gone well. There had been one little blip with the blood pressure, but it had settled down. There is nothing to say why she might have gone into labour early, and it is a little late to ask if this is common in her family, we can only press on. I manage to examine her abdominally between contractions. The baby is lying well if a little posterior; with all its limbs a little to the front, the labour could be a rather slow, but it feels to be a small baby, as expected by its dates, so it should present no problems. I am a little concerned when I listen to the baby's heart; from high on the abdomen the beat sounds different to when I listen to it lower down. Mrs Macaronis' abdomen is much distended and I am concerned that there might be a lot of water around the baby, this I do not like.

4.15 p.m.

The membranes rupture, there is little fluid, or no more than I would expect. The baby's heartbeat sounds loud and clear, but in the brief moments I have between contractions, I can still hear its echo. All I can do is deliver the baby; if there is anything wrong there are enough people around to dash for help, and I had seen a telephone on a table next door.

5.05 p.m.

Mrs Macaronis has pushed for almost an hour. The elderly lady, who was in the room when I arrived, has been and gone several times. On each visit she has brought with her drinks of fruit-flavoured water, not only for Mrs Macaronis and her sister, but also for me. I think that I will soon have to visit the toilet, but this is not the moment: the baby's head is born. The body follows with no problem, and Mrs Macaronis has her son. It is a small infant, and its coating of white oil denotes that it is a little premature.

The cry of the infant and the news shouted from the doorway brings Mr Macaronis, who enters the room followed by a rousing cheer. He descends upon his wife, and covering her in a blanket of alcohol fumes and kisses, he talks faster than I am sure any language should allow. Now he turns to his son. I have checked the heart, it is fine, I can hear no second beat, but I will ask Mr Macaronis to contact the doctor straight away just to make sure. But I have little time to say anything. I have wrapped the baby in a dressing towel ready to pass to his mother, but it is Mr Macaronis who receives him in both hands. Opening the towel just to make sure that he has a son, he lets out a cry of joy, and then, having kissed his son, he holds him out in front of him, and passes through the open door to a cheer from the assembled crowd in the other room.

5.25 p.m.

I had followed Mr Macaronis with my eyes, and now, pulling down my mask, I turn towards the mother, firstly, to apologise to her for not giving her the baby to hold, and secondly, to ask her sister to go and reclaim the baby. But Mrs Macaronis is paying no attention to me, nor is her sister. Mrs Macaronis appears to be still in labour and the present contraction is very strong. Sometimes the contractions seem to start again when the afterbirth is delivered; I hope that Mrs Macaronis is not going to have difficulty in delivering the afterbirth. I step to her side and, placing my hand on her abdomen, I press. I expect to feel a flaccid collapsed uterus, but there is nothing of the sort, the uterus is still enlarged. Frantically I search in my discarded bag for the foetal stethoscope. I just catch the beat before the next contraction starts; there is another baby in the uterus.

Now I understand the echoed beat, it did not belong to the baby who has been delivered, it belongs to his sibling. I call out to the mother as I frantically search the bag for clean gloves, forceps, scissors and a dressing towel.

'Mrs Macaronis, you are going to have another baby, you have twins.'

Mrs Macaronis is not listening; she is busy pushing, I have little time to examine her to find out which part of the baby is presenting, just a quick moment when the uterus relaxes reassures me that the head is coming first.

5.45 p.m.

The door has opened behind me. Mr Macaronis stands beside me and watches the birth of his second son in awe.

6.30 p.m.

The second child is a little smaller than his brother; I will know exactly how much smaller when I weigh them, but now I know why the birth was premature, there were two good-sized babies present.

I sit at the far end of the bedroom and bath them. They both weigh over five pounds. The guests had gone quiet when the announcement of a second baby was made, but on the announcement of a second son they had gone mad, I had been obliged to ask for a little quiet for the sake of the babies. I am sure that they will have to get used to such noise, but maybe a little quiet will be good this early in life. Mr Macaronis is in a daze, I think that he has had so many drinks to wet his sons' heads that he can hardly stand. He has been in and out of the room, and has looked at his sons several times, each time he comes he touches them just to make sure that they are real. But he won't hold them; when I asked him if he wished to he had replied in Italian, and then correcting himself he said, 'Oh no, nurse, I have taken too much drink, I might hurt them they are so small, their mother will care for them.'

Mrs Macaronis is resting and, after having drunk two small glasses of brandy, one for each of her sons, she is asleep. She had donned a lace bed jacket and, holding a child in each arm, she had been photographed. Grandma and great aunt have been photographed with the babies and Mr Macaronis had been talked into sitting beside his wife for the first family portrait.

7.00 p.m.

I examine the placenta as I stand in a cold room at the back of the house. Mr Macaronis had said that I should look at the placenta in the bedroom; that it should not be taken out into the cold as it was a part of his sons' previous life. I managed to assure him that his sons would no longer need it and that it might make a considerable mess on the carpet if I didn't take it away, so here I am with my rubber gloves covered in blood in the stone-floored room. I am sure there is only one placenta; the twins are identical.

8.30 p.m.

The kitchen is cold – in fact the whole flat is cold. I climb the stairs with heavy legs and Mrs Stone meets me in the hall as I wheel in my bike. There had been a call just after I had left, probably one of the cases that was due today. Mrs Stone had redirected the call to Miss Wilkins, who had rung about ten minutes ago to ask why I had not yet contacted her. I threw the used bag and the gas and air machine into the clinical room. I would attend to them after I had had a cup of tea and after I had rung Miss Wilkins.

9.15 p.m.

I put down the phone. My ear aches. Miss Wilkins certainly takes her responsibilities seriously. I had only managed to quiet her by reminding her that another lady is due to deliver any time now and might be trying to contact me as we talk. The only thing that I had gained from the call was a reminder that I now have two first-day post-natals to attend tomorrow morning, unless of course I have another delivery tonight, and then I will have three.

9.20 p.m.

Standing in the kitchen I am making myself something to eat. I pour the contents of a glass jar into a saucepan – it smells delicious and I am very hungry. I had tried to give Mr Macaronis the news about the twins, but he was too involved with his guests. I had managed to direct his sister into the bedroom and had told her. I had also told her that Mrs Macaronis and the babies might now welcome a little quiet and that the babies would need a good deal of care over the next few days.

Mr Macaronis had entered the bedroom with a smile across his face that stretched from ear to ear. The young woman with the beautiful hair had followed him, and she carried several wine glasses and a bottle of wine.

'The guests are leaving; I have had enough of a birthday celebration already,' Mr Macaronis had said.

It was then that I realised that the twins had imposed upon their father's fortieth birthday party. A glass of wine had been placed in my hand and a toast to the babies had been drunk. Mr Macaronis then held up his glass again and proposed another toast.

'To Pupil Midwife Compton, who has brought me all that a man can desire, two sons.'

The five women and two men who were in the room raised their glasses and called, 'To Pupil Midwife Compton.' My glass had been refilled and now I sit with my head in my hands feeling quite exhausted. I had reiterated the need for care with such small babies, but, as grandma and grand-aunt, who were obviously more experienced than I, had descended on the infants, I felt it safe to leave as infant care Italian-style was being organised. A bag had hung from my handlebars when I peddled back up the road and now I have every intention of devouring the contents of the jar that lay in it.

15

Sunday 15th April

3.30 a.m.

The bell calls, and by its third ring I am holding the earpiece to my ear and am speaking to the caller. 'Pupil Midwife Compton here, can I help you?'

The voice is quiet and muffled. I can hardly hear it. I call out again, 'Mrs O'Reilly's house, Pupil Midwife Compton speaking.'

The voice, now a little louder, interrupts me, 'Is that the nurse? Oh dear, umm, nurse, Mrs Waller is going to have the baby, can you come?'

I hasten to reassure the speaker, 'Yes Mr Waller, I will come, please tell me the address to come to.'

Clearing his throat noisily, he continues, 'We live on Montgomery Street, about halfway down it, that is if you start from the top of the road, if you start from the bottom we live halfway up it. Hello, are you there, nurse?'

'Yes, Mr Waller, I am here, if you leave . . .'

The line goes dead. I was going to suggest he leave lights on in the front of house so that I will know which one it is but I remember that the number of the house will be recorded in the notes. This is one of the cases that I had expected and as I fight my way past the dirty delivery bag and the half-used gas and air machine, the notes soon come to hand. I know where the house is as I have been there before. All the road names on the new council estate where the Wallers live are named after World War Two heroes, or Labour MPs.

Mrs Stone is standing at the bottom of the stairs; she must have ears like a bat.

'If anything else comes, I'll direct it to Miss Wilkins for you, having a busy time, aren't you?'

She smiles at me as I set off with the loaded bike.

3.45 a.m.

The streets by the park are in complete darkness, I can just make out the line of the metal railings that edge the park and run along the opposite side of the road on which I now travel. I have switched on my bike lamps, but the front light keeps flickering on and off. I had intended to get some new batteries yesterday afternoon, but events had taken over. A figure looms towards me; I can just make out a shape as it crosses the road from the park. I give the front light a thump with my gloved hand, and for a moment the beam lights up the figure of a man and a large dog. The dog barks a deep throaty bark and a man's voice, equally deep and throaty, calls, 'Shut up'. A thickset young man with close-cropped hair stands in the beam of the light, which chooses this moment to extinguish itself. I am pleased to find someone who might tell me the way, but I am a little worried as to whether this is exactly the person to ask at this time of the night. However, my worries are soon allayed when, pulling the dog behind him, the young man asks, 'You lost there then, nurse? I saw a bike coming along, thought that's too small for a cop, must be an angel of mercy on a mission.'

He laughs at his own joke, and I have time to speak.

'Oh good morning, yes, I am rather lost. I'm looking for Montgomery Street.'

My attention to my plight wavers as the dog, having

moved out from behind its master's legs, now sniffs at my back tyre. Having satisfied itself that my bike is a suitable place to leave a marker, it turns itself around, lifts its back leg and relieves itself against the spokes of my back wheel. I am pleased to note that it misses the delivery bag and my shoe. My attention is returned to its master as I hear him speak.

'So, do you think that you'll be able to find it?'

I look up at his face, I had not heard a word that he had said. He looks back at me and shakes his head sideways.

'Oh women, you lot could get lost on a postage stamp, come on I'll walk down with you.'

He turns and sets off down the road. I follow him and the dog walks behind him, nearly tripping its master up as it attempts to sniff at my front tyre. I am relieved when he pulls the dog over and makes it walk by his other leg. The young man now stops at a junction in the road. The dog comes back around his legs and places its nose on my front wheel.

'There's Montgomery Street, nurse, think you might find the number you want on your own?'

Keeping my eye on his dog, I assure him that I will manage that and, thanking him, I press my foot down on the pedal and set off before the dog can make up its mind to mark my front wheel as well.

I see a lighted window; it stands out in the row of dark houses that line the street on both sides. I had passed another intersection and had searched for a road name but there were none, all had already been removed, so the sight of a lighted window is very welcome, I can only hope that I am still on Montgomery Street.

3.55 a.m.

A young man in his shirtsleeves answers the door. His hair is tousled and his eyes are wide. I have little need to ask if he is Mr Waller, but I do reassure myself. Having laid claim to my bike he follows me into what I think to be a small square room. I can see little as the room is in darkness, except for a diffused light that comes through an open door at the far corner of the room. The atmosphere in the room feels strange. I can't put my finger on what is wrong, but after the cold night air I find it hard to breathe. Propping my bike against the wall, the man passes me and, heading for the half-open door, he calls over his shoulder, 'Can you come in here, nurse, and see if I have everything?'

As I near the door I realise what is wrong; the air is full of steam, and as he opens the door and we enter what I assume to be the kitchen it becomes almost impossible to breathe. There is a light on somewhere in the room, lighting up the water vapour that fills the air. Gasping for breath, I turn my head back into the room I have just left. At least there is still a little air in there. I hear the man speaking, although it is hard to see him.

'Do you think there is enough here, nurse? If you want some more I can get another saucepan.'

Undoing the top button of my coat, I step towards the voice. A gas stove stands in the corner between walls that are running with rivers of water, and as my eyes accustom themselves to the humidity, I see the contents of the stove and the cause of the wetness. A large galvanised bucket, standing on one of the stove's back burners, is full to the brim with water that is boiling furiously; beside it a large saucepan competes to boil faster; and on one of the front burners a kettle blows out steam. The young man gives me a worried look.

'If you want, I can put on another saucepan?'

For a moment I am lost for words and then I realise that all of this water is being boiled for my use, so, trying to regain my breath and my wits, I try to reassure him.

'Oh I think that we have plenty of boiling water here, Mr Waller, in fact it might be advisable to turn off the gas under the bucket until I see your wife. I will have to see when she might have the baby, we don't want all the water to boil away before we need it, do we?'

He looks at me with startled eyes as he grabs a bowl from the sink, and almost shouts in my face, 'I can always fill them back up, nurse.'

I must take the law into my own hands before the whole house becomes awash, so, leaning forward, I turn off the gas under the bucket and, as it stops boiling, I turn and smile at Mr Waller.

'That will be absolutely brilliant; just what I will need, boiled water that has cooled down a little.'

I wait for him to turn off the saucepan and the kettle but they continue to boil, but at least we have halved the steam output.

4.10 a.m.

I have retrieved the delivery bag and the gas and air machine and they now stand at the bottom of the bed in the rather overcrowded small bedroom. Mrs Waller, a mousey little woman, lies on a double bed which takes up much of the space in the room. A child's cot is squeezed in the space between the bed and the wall. I have determined that Mrs Waller is in labour, and I now look for some-where to lay out my equipment. There is no table in the room. I ask Mrs Waller if there is one available, but as I look across at her I realise that a 'Yes, nurse' from her did not mean that she had understood the request. I had assumed too much. The door opens and Mr Waller enters. He walks sideways and holds the door open with his elbow as he presents me with a flower-patterned china cup. The elbow lets go of the door and the flowered saucer follows its companion. Pushing his hand into his trouser pocket he produces an almost empty sugar bag and from his other pocket he produces a spoon. Without speaking or looking at me, he spoons sugar into the cup, which I now hold on its saucer and, having stirred the tea and returned the spoon and sugar into their appointed places, he steps backwards. Nodding my thanks, I drink the tea. It is very welcome as it my first today. I turn to ask Mr Waller if he has a table that might be brought into the room, but before I can speak he relieves me of the cup, which I am just raising to my lips and, taking the saucer from my other hand, he is gone.

I need the table as I want to lay out some equipment. I must examine Mrs Waller, and I will need some of Mr Waller's boiling water. In the kitchen the steam has subsided somewhat, but the humidity is still high, and Mr Waller still attends his utensils. A Formica-topped kitchen table stands in the corner of the room, and I lean my hand on it as I make my request.

'Mr Waller, I need to have a table in the bedroom, I need . . .'

I get no further. Swiping everything off the table he lifts it, and whether it will fit in the stairwell or not, it is carried up to the bedroom. I follow the scrape marks as it disappears before me. We manage to fit it in between the bed and the window, but passage around the bed is now impossible. The banging has awakened a child who now stands leaning over the side of its cot, reviewing the proceedings over a large rubber soother, which wags up and down across its face.

I have examined Mrs Waller and labour is well advanced. The baby should be on its way within the hour so I decide to wait with her. The door opens and Mr Waller enters. As before, he carries a cup in one hand and saucer in the other. This time I drink the tea in one move; I had only managed half a cup last time. I write up the notes. All is well, and the child, who stands in the cot, I am told, is a boy of eighteen months. He quietly watches all and seems to make no demands of either parent.

4.45 a.m.

Mrs Waller is using the gas and air machine and labour is progressing well. She had not made much noise, but now the contractions are strong and she calls out as she grabs for the mask. The door opens and Mr Waller enters. I am expecting him to be carrying another cup of tea, and I am not disappointed. I start to say that it would be better if he sat by his wife and helped her with the gas and air, but he pushes the cup and the sugar at me and then, retrieving them, is gone. Mrs Waller calls out, the child, who watches her with care, looks rather startled at his mother's obvious discomfort and starts to cry. I need Mr Waller's help. In gown and mask I fall down the stairs. As I go I hear the child start to scream. Mr Waller is still attending to his duties at the stove and I call out as I reach the bottom of the stairs.

'Mr Waller, can you come upstairs, I need your help.'

He looks at me like a startled rabbit in the headlights of a car; I need to get through the fog in the room and in his brain, so I shout, 'Mr Waller, please come upstairs to your wife.'

He follows me and, as we turn to climb, the child's

screaming stops abruptly. As I enter the bedroom, I can smell the sweet familiar smell of nitrous oxide; is the cylinder leaking? That is the last thing I need. But no, Mrs Waller is sucking hard on it. The child no longer leans over the cot side, and all is silent. What has happened? How has Mrs Waller managed this? With one knee on the bottom of the bed, I push myself across it, and resting on my hands and knees I peer into the cot. The child lies on his back with his head to one side; he is fast asleep. The smell I know well lingers over him, and I realise why I could smell nitrous oxide. I finish my journey across the bed in one bound, and drop at the end of the cot. Lowering its side I scoop the child in my arms, he hangs limp, his head against my chest and his arms and legs hanging down. Laying him across the bed I hastily place my head against his chest, the heart is beating loud and clear if a little fast, the smell of the gas is on his breath. What must I do? I must get some air into him to clear out the gas.

'Mr Waller, Mr Waller, help me, for heaven's sake throw open the window.'

For a moment he hesitates, then, leaning over the table, he swings the window open. His son lies on the table and, as I lift his arms above his head several times, his face screws up and as he breaths an enormous sigh, he starts to cough. I pick him up and hold him to me. With relief I hear him gulping in air as cries shudder through him. Mrs Waller shouts out, 'I have to push, nurse.'

I pass the still-sobbing child across the table to his father.

5.15 a.m.

Mrs Waller gives birth to a baby girl with little difficulty.

6.30 a.m.

I have drunk several more cups of tea, the baby has been bathed in warm well-boiled water, and Mrs Waller is comfortable. I ask her what had happened to Benny, the little boy. She smiles up at me over the rim of the chipped mug.

'Oh, I thought his crying might upset you, nurse, so I gave him a whiff of the mask.'

Apparently, keeping her finger over the hole, she had put the mask over the child's face. Unfortunately, he had drawn in a large breath ready for his next scream, but fortunately he had taken only one breath, which had been enough to knock him over and away from the mask.

After drinking a large bottle of milk, Benny has gone to sleep, and I have reassured myself several times that his sleep is normal. I have asked Mr Waller to tell the doctor what happened with Benny when he comes to see Mrs Waller and the new baby. I am not sure if Mr Waller will remember, or even if the doctor will come.

6.45 a.m.

I wheel the bike out through the door. The street lights are on and dawn starts to lighten the sky. Mr Waller holds the broken gate open and, as I pass through, he speaks to the pavement just in front of me.

'Did I do all right, nurse? The men at work said that you would want a lot of water boiling and you would leave me to it if I didn't boil enough.'

Then for the first time he looks me in the face and smiles a smile of brown uneven teeth.

'Must have done all right, you didn't leave, did you? You didn't fall to sleep either, so I must have done OK with the tea.'

With the smile still firmly attached, he turns, and with jaunty step re-enters his now, not quite so steamy, house.

I look after him. So all the boiling water and the tea making had been due to wisecracking men who wanted to play a gag on their mate. For a moment I feel angry. I had wanted Mr Waller to help me, not to boil water, but a disaster with his son had been averted, so although I planned revenge as I peddled my way back to the flat, I decided that I had better leave Mr Waller to deal with his workmates in his own way.

7.00 a.m.

Mrs Stone meets me as I enter the hall. Miss Wilkins had rung ten minutes ago, and had asked if I had yet been to see the woman who she had delivered. Mrs Stone looks at me with sad eyes as she passes on the message.

'She said would you please ring her as soon as you come in as she is very busy, and she can't hang around waiting for you to make up your mind to contact her.'

Her smile is weak as she finishes and, as I drag the bag and the gas and air box along the hall, she speaks to my back.

'I'll make you a cup of tea and a bacon sandwich while you call her.'

7.45 a.m.

I have given a blow-by-blow account, well almost blow-by-blow, of both deliveries, and I have received same on the one I missed. Miss Wilkins is nothing if not thorough, and she takes her responsibilities very seriously.

The sandwich was most welcome, and now I must attack the disaster zone; Mrs O'Reilly will have a fit if she sees the clinical room in the state that I have left it in at the moment. But first I had better visit Mrs Bloom, and check on Miss Wilkins's delivery.

The Blooms live on the other side of the park, or maybe I should say on the other side of the track. Their house is semi-detached and bay-windowed. I can imagine that there are many complaints about the council tenants who inhabit the far side of the green space. Mother and baby are well, and I listen as a multitude of praises are heaped on Miss Wilkins.

10.30 a.m.

Mrs Stone again meets me in the hallway; not another delivery, I hope, but no, Mr Macaronis has rung and asked if I will visit his wife. I had intended to visit this morning, but I want to clean the clinical room before I go. However, I cannot ignore the call, it may be urgent.

3.00 p.m.

The hot water feels lovely as I slide into it; it seems like years ago that I had time to relax in the bath. I had ridden down to see the Macaronis twins as soon as I received the message. It had been quite a journey after the ride to the Bloom's house but I had been concerned that something had happened to one, or both, of the small boys, and I didn't want to waste any time in getting to them. But when I had arrived it was Mrs Macaronis who presented the problem. The family had had a restless night. The twins had taken it in turns to cry, and Mrs Macaronis had been convinced that it was her inability to breast feed that had caused the trouble. I had taken some time to find a chemist shop which was open, and to buy some feeding bottles and food. The whole process had not been helped by Mr Macaronis' mother; she could not reconcile herself to the fact that offspring of her family might have to have 'artificial milk', as she called it. I had managed to convince her that her daughter-in-law could be forgiven, as she was trying to feed two babies, and not just one. Baby Giovanni and baby Joshua had settled down after a little drink of half-cream Cow and Gate milk and some peace and quiet, and I had left with two bottles of Italian wine, one from each twin. It had rained when I was on my way home so I had decided to take a bath and wash my hair before I sorted out the clinical room.

4.00 p.m.

There is a sudden, loud rat-a-tat sound, and for a moment I can't think where I am. A white coloured sheet spreads out in front of my eyes, and something stiff seems to press down on my lower jaw. The rat-a-tat comes again, and I attempt to move my legs which seem to be weighed down. Something cold hits me in the face, and I have difficulty in sitting up, everything beneath me is slippery. Now I realise, I am lying in a bath of cold water. Fighting to sit upright, I lose my balance and, rolling over, I go face first into the lukewarm water. The banging on the door becomes louder and, to add to my horror, it is Mrs O'Reilly's voice that calls out.

'Nurse Compton, are you in there? Are you all right?'

The banging now gets louder, and as I reach hand and knees level, I attempt to call out, but no voice comes. Grasping the edge of the bath I try to pull to a standing position. The soap has been left in the water and has become lodged under my foot. My feet slide back down the bath, and as I vainly grab at the bath sides. I see the cold murky water come over my face. Gasping for breath I manage to crawl out on my hands and knees. Now I hear other voices. Mrs Stone says, 'She was all right this morning when I saw her, just looked a bit tired.'

Now Mr Stone's voice asks, 'Do you want me to break the door in? I can give it a punch if you like.'

Mrs O'Reilly's voice intercedes, 'No, let me give her another shout first.'

With the towel wrapped around me I throw open the door, and Mrs O'Reilly is shouting into my face.

'Nurse Compton, are you . . . ?'

I smile sheepishly at the assembled group and, as water drips off my hair and down my face, I try to smile.

'Sorry, I fell asleep.'

Three pairs of eyes look at me, and I'm not sure whether I see relief or anger there.

4.15 p.m.

In ten minutes I am in a clean uniform and am upstairs in the kitchen. Mrs O'Reilly is reading her newspaper, drinking a cup of tea.

'There's one in the pot.'

She speaks without looking at me and, helping myself to a drink, I sit and wait for her to make the next move. After what seems like a long time, she puts down her paper, looks at me, and speaks. 'Well, I had imagined all kinds of things that might have happened over the last two days, and I had imagined many situations that might face me when I returned, but this state of affairs had never entered my head. But there we are, I suppose it's rather like having a puppy dog in the house, you never know what they are going to do next.'

Lifting her newspaper she stands, and I stand.

'I assume that you have yet to finish your work.'

With the cold remark she is gone, and I hear the sitting-room door close behind her. I stare at the table top; it becomes bubbly and indistinct as the first tear runs down my face. I had felt proud of myself; not many midwives get to deliver twins, and I had dealt with Mr Waller and his strange behaviour. The bottles of wine gleam red under the overhead light, and now, for a moment, I feel angry. I had worked hard and I was tired, so I fell asleep, so what? For a moment I consider going into the sitting-room and asking her how she dare call me a puppy dog, but then I realise that she is right, it was a stupid thing to do.

4.35 p.m.

The clinical room is in a mess. I now have to admit that it was a good thing that another call hadn't come through; I would have been hard put to know which gas and air machine to take, and the only clean delivery bag lay at the back of the room; it had been packed about two weeks ago.

5.15 p.m.

Notes have been written and returned to their appropriate place and the sterilizer comes to the boil for the second time; order is being restored. The door opens and Mrs O'Reilly enters. I glance across at her, much of my face hidden behind a mask. She looks at me down her long nose, her eyes part hidden behind steam-fogged glasses.

'If you would bring up the appropriate notes we can look at them in the sitting-room before we eat, I assume that you have not eaten yet today.'

As she speaks she glances around the room, grunts to

herself, and then leaves, closing the door behind her with a firm click. At least we are on professional terms again.

5.45 p.m.

The light is on and, as I enter the room, I smell wine. One of my bottles stands on the small coffee table with its cork drawn. We sit across the table under the window; Mrs O'Reilly makes small alterations and additions to the notes as we talk.

'I will pop down and see the twins tomorrow. That was quite some achievement; I bet there will be some red faces at the antenatal clinic tomorrow.'

She laughs when I tell her about Mr Waller, and agrees that we must handle the case with care. We have finished the discussion, and I have left Benny out of it, although he has surfaced to the tip of my tongue a few times. Reproaching myself I have not mentioned the affair, her voice breaks through my troubled thoughts.

'You know you must never be unattainable when you are on duty. If you are not attainable, then you must always make sure that someone knows where you are.'

I start to make my excuses, but as the eyes look at me through their thick glasses, I know that she is right.

'If you are tired then take a proper rest, but make sure that you can hear the phone, even when you are in the bath. Now I am assuming that this rather good wine is a gift from your Italian clients, so I suggest we start on it, and celebrate their birth.'

Benny's face flashes before me, and I see his limp body lying on the bed. Trying to cover my agitation, I stand as I speak.

'I had intended to go back and see Mrs Waller this evening, I am not sure if those two are up to looking after so small a baby.'

My face feels hot, and I turn my back on the table.

'It's your case, you must do what you think fit, but do please keep me informed of any problems or unusual circumstances.'

Once again I know that she knows, she can read my mind, she knows I have something to hide, I turn and face her.

6.10 p.m.

The black Austin car stands by the kerb on Montgomery Street. It is still daylight and children play on the street. Several young boys are around the car as we alight, and a voice calls out, 'Good evening, nurse. Charlie, you keep away from that car or I'll knock your head off when you get home.'

With socks hanging around thin legs the boys back away from the car and, slinking sideways, they burst into roars of laughter as they turn and run. The large lady moves her shopping bag from one hand to the other, and bottles clink as she nods her head and shoulders towards the Waller's house.

'Had a girl last night, so I hear, hope nothing's wrong, nurse.'

She looks from Mrs O'Reilly to me and back again, her canny eyes looking for any sign hesitation that might lend force to gossip. Putting her hand on my back, and propelling me towards the gate, Mrs O'Reilly turns to the newsmonger.

'Ah, I'm pleased to see you, Mrs Potts, I saw your doctor the other day, he said that you had not been to see him about your Jimmy's eye, he must have that squint dealt with you know.'

I smile to myself as I knock at the door; Mrs Potts is certainly losing that battle. The door opens and Mr

Waller, in shirtsleeves, looks at me with the same bemused look that he had left me with earlier this morning, and I am overjoyed to see Benny hanging onto his leg. He takes us upstairs. Mrs O'Reilly is introduced all round and the follow-up visit is entered in the notes. Benny is quite happy when I hold him and he pats his father on the top of his head as he walks down the stairs before us.

8.45 p.m.

The twins' birth is celebrated with the opened wine. Nothing is said about Benny until I am retiring, and then as I say, 'Goodnight'.

Mrs O'Reilly replies, 'Goodnight, Benny looks fine, thank you for telling me.'

16

Wednesday 18th April

2.35 p.m.

I have only one more case completed, which makes five in all. I sit while my tutor peruses the latest entry in my schedule, I know that there will be more explaining to do, and here it comes.

'Nurse Compton, I am, once again, unable to follow this case through. There seems to be rather a lack of preparatory examination, and some rather extended periods between the stages of the delivery.'

I take in a big breath; yes, however she might word it, Mrs Clarke's delivery was not of the conventional.

I start to speak, but Miss Perkins has not finished.

'I see that she had a post-partum haemorrhage, did you ring for the flying squad?'

I squeeze my words in quickly, 'No, Miss Perkins, we, I mean, I, sent for an ambulance.'

Her eyes rest on my face for some moments before she speaks. I remember Mrs O'Reilly's instructions, answer only questions asked.

'But she is well now?'

The question catches me unawares.

'Yes, after a blood transfusion and a sterilisation, she was home in three days.'

Too much information given, I had lost three days of the post-partum care, and now my face burns red. Would the delivery be disallowed, would I have to remove it from my schedule? Sighing, Miss Perkins looks down at my notes.

'You have only three cases completed, Nurse Compton, you must have twelve completed and written in your schedule before May 21st or you will not be entered for the examination, I hope you understand this.'

I nod, but I am unsure what I can do about it. My only consolation is that I have three more cases yet to complete, and one of them is a twin delivery.

The weather has turned warmer and Tony has rung to ask if I would like to play tennis after the tutorials. He is sitting his finals in June, so recreation time is short and precious. I have asked Mrs O'Reilly if it would be okay if I am a couple of hours late. She said that I should remember that I am on duty that evening, but she thought a little change of activity might do me good.

4.00 p.m.

Tony stands by the tennis courts, he looks tall and handsome in his tennis whites, and my heart skips a beat as I dance towards him, my borrowed racquet raised high in salutation. There are three courts, they stand empty and pristine clean, their red surfaces are smooth and clearly marked, ready for the summer's use. We head for the court furthest from the entrance gate, and start to knock up. Tony is a good player and soon my white plimsolls and ankle socks are turning red with dust as I race and slide to return his shots. The metal gate clicks and, as I retrieve balls from the middle court, I see two young men take up position on the court at the far end. The game continues, and we call to each other, each determined not to lose the upper hand. The metal gate clicks again, this time I do not see who enters, but as I move across to retrieve the stray balls I am faced by an elegant young woman. She stands tall and straight, her shiny new racquet is held out at an angle from her body and her other hand smooths down her trim, white skirt. She looks down her nose at me, and makes no attempt to help me to retrieve our balls. I retrieve them and, mumbling my thanks and apologies, I return to the game. Out of the corner of my eye I see them standing at the net, not an unusual thing to do, maybe they are discussing who will serve first, but then the young man leaves the net, walks to the back of the court and, turning at an angle, walks onto our court. Tony is just preparing to serve but stops at the intrusion. The two men speak as they each look across at me in turn. I am standing in a crouching position waiting for Tony's serve; I stand upright, what has happened?

Tony's face is very red as he turns back towards me, but it is not the red of exertion. Turning away from me he stoops and gathers up the balls. I look in amazement, what has happened? His voice sounds harsh as he shouts, 'Collect the balls while I put the net down.'

Lost in amazement, I turn to gather up the balls, the tall girl is patting a bright yellow ball over the net, her foot is raised behind her in a prissy manner and, as she swings from the net, her eyes meet mine, and her face holds what I can only describe as a triumphant smirk. Tony is heading for the exit gate, and I follow at speed, what has happened? Is he needed on the wards? Is a relative ill? I catch up with him as he heads towards the hospital buildings. I was just about to ask what had happened when he swings around on me.

'You had to make a fool of me, didn't you, you know that this is an all-white club, and you have to try and push yourself in wearing those ridiculous shorts.'

I stop in my tracks, my shorts are green and white

checked, I had not brought any tennis gear with me when I came on this course, and when Tony had phoned to ask if I would play I had nipped into a shop and had bought the nearest I could get to white. I had even gone to the lengths of buying new plimsolls. Now, as I stand and watch Tony's retreating figure, even his back exudes anger. He turns to face me as he reaches one of the many doors into the hospital, and spits in anger, 'That was our senior house officer and the Prof's daughter, I just love being shown up in front of such people.'

He is gone, and I can do nothing but change and head home. I go into the Students Union building to return the racquet; I am surprised when Tony calls out to me as I am leaving.

'Dot, you still coming on Saturday?'

I nod yes; he nods his head and is gone.

6.00 p.m.

I climb the stairs, everything seems to be going wrong, I have the least number of deliveries of anyone on the course, maybe I won't even be able to enter for my exams, and now I don't know what to think about Tony. I had been looking forward to the party on Saturday but now I have my doubts. I had not looked for a doctor as a boyfriend, I had always been determined to stay clear of them as some of my friends in general training had been treated badly by them. With these thoughts in mind, I walk into the kitchen. Mrs O'Reilly looks up from the oven.

'Thought I heard you coming, good heavens what has happened? You have a face as long as last week. Was it that last case? I tell you, those hospital midwives live in cuckoo land.'

She sucks in her breath as she stops speaking, and

quickly drops a large pie-dish on the table. I smile to myself, maybe I am just very hungry, and who cares about that snobby lot anyway.

'Oh, just a bit of moaning, but I got away with it.'

She throws two plates onto the table, and plunges a long knife into the pie crust.

Mrs O'Reilly carries on, 'Got away with it, I should think that they might have noticed some pretty good work there, but then that might have been too much to ask for.'

As steam rises from the two plates I feel better, and I speak between mouthfuls of Mrs Stone's delicious meat and potato pie.

'The tutor said that I should start being concerned about the number of cases that I have completed; she's worried that I won't be able to enter for the exam.'

After a few seconds Mrs O'Reilly replies, 'Has she got nothing else to worry about, we've got a Tory Government back, the country is in chaos, and all she can do is worry you unnecessarily. Next time tell her we still know how to be good breeders around here.'

As she finishes speaking the phone rings, and she laughs as she says, 'There you are, one of the breeders ringing now.'

Pushing my plate from me I hasten to the phone, but it is not a breeder, it is one of Mrs O'Reilly's friends. I put her unfinished dinner in the oven and, with a lighter heart, I finish eating mine.

8.00 p.m.

I have put on my dressing-gown and I slide my feet into bed, I have been reminded that I don't have many cases, and I most certainly know that the Part Two exams are looming. The exam is a viva, and it can last anything from half to three quarters of an hour. You can be asked a lot of things in half an hour. Now I feel warm, and I have found the place where I need to read; the phone rings.

I hear a man's voice speaking, but I can't understand a word that he is saying.

'Hello this is the midwife's house, Pupil Midwife Compton speaking, may I help you?'

He speaks with a very strong accent, and he sounds as though he is drunk. I cannot understand him. I try again.

'This is Pupil Midwife Compton speaking, could you please give me your name.'

Sounds pour out of the earpiece, I try to sort out some useful words, but I can still understand nothing. The phone goes dead. I wait in case the caller tries again, but nothing happens.

Tentatively, I tap on the sitting-room door, I don't want to disturb Mrs O'Reilly as she has few visitors, and I would like to sort this out myself, but I have no clue where to start. I hear laughter and then a voice calls 'Come in.'

I explain what has happened. Excusing herself, Mrs O'Reilly rises and we leave the room together. At the top of the stairs she halts and, wiping cake crumbs from her mouth, she speaks, 'Go and get into uniform while I see if I can sort out who it might be.'

I return, buttoning my dress as I enter the clinical room. Mrs O'Reilly is poring over a couple of sets of notes.

'Did he sound as though he had had a few drinks?'

She speaks as she turns over a set of notes. I hesitate for a moment, I don't want to lose the case, if I say that he sounded well under the influence she might think that I will not be able to manage alone. I need this case so I reply with care.

'Well, I'm not sure, he might have been slurring, but he certainly wasn't speaking English.'

She turns the set of notes over again.

'There is a Mrs Copperopolis who might be due about

now. Oh Lordie she's another of Mrs Quinn's cases. I've been to see her several times but I've only managed to get her in once and I didn't get to examine her then. I don't know a lot about her other than it's her second baby. According to Mrs Quinn, her husband can put the Greek brandy away.'

She has been talking to the notes, and now she hands them to me.

'According to her notes she's not due for a couple of weeks, but she is the only one I can find to fit the bill. Bit of a ride, but go down and see, ring me if it isn't her, I'll hang on here in case. Have you got some change on you?'

She shouts the last words at me as I leave the room, notes in hand. I smile over my shoulder, and pat my pocket.

8.20 p.m.

It is still twilight as I cycle into the small, overgrown garden of the large house that fronts onto the main road into town. The house is on the boundary of Mrs Quinn's area, so is a little way out of town. There are two bells at the side of the large door which stands a couple of steps up from the broken drive. I ring one of them. I hear the sound of the bell echoing in the house but no one replies. I try the other bell, and after what seems like an eternity the door starts to open. A woman in a large dressing-gown appears in the open doorway. Mumbling something that I cannot understand, she turns and heads back through the door. Is it she who has rung for me, or is she just annoyed at being disturbed at this time in the evening? I cannot even tell if she is pregnant under the bulky dressing-gown. Hastily pushing my bike behind a bush growing under the bay window, I grab my bag and follow her; no good bringing the gas and air machine, this could be a false alarm.

The hall is in semi-darkness now that I have closed the door behind me. There are doors to my left and right; both are closed. Stairs rise in darkness just beyond the door to my right and, as a light snaps on in a room to the left of the stairs, I see a heavy hall stand blocking my way. My shoes click on tiles as I tentatively make my way towards the light. The room is quite large, but it is not of the same proportions as those in the houses further down the road, but as I step around the door, it feels as cold as they do. The only window lets in little light from the back of the house, and the large ornately fringed light-shade largely shadows the light bulb. The woman leans on a dressing table and clutches her abdomen. I don't understand a word she says but I now make the assumption that I am in the right house and, putting down my bag, I hasten to her side as I speak.

'I am Pupil Midwife Compton, how often are the contractions coming, Mrs Copperopolis?'

She raises her hand to silence me as the contraction continues, but at least she had responded to the name so I can assume that I have the right patient and that the right set of notes rest in the bag. I take off my coat and place it over a chair that stands by a large dark wood wardrobe. As I look around for some form of heating, I see none. A deep voice speaks behind me.

'They are every two or three minutes nurse, I asked him to ring an hour ago, but at least he did ring, and you are here.'

The dressing-gown has fallen open, and I can now see that she is a woman of short stature who has a wide girth; 'A quick delivery with those hips,' I think to myself. Dropping the dressing-gown behind her she climbs onto the large double bed and, almost before she has settled, the next contraction starts. Hanging onto the dark wooden uprights of the bed, she curses in what I assume to be Greek. As the contraction ends, I place the foetal stethoscope on her abdomen in search of the baby's heart.

I more smell him than see him at first, but as I look sideways from the abdomen a figure appears around the door. The light is not bright, and the vision seems almost surreal as it waves gently from side to side. Having found the baby's heartbeat, maybe a little higher up the abdomen than I might have expected, I turn my attention to the apparition which is now working its way around the bed towards me. Before it reaches me, Mrs Copperopolis rises up, shouts words I do not understand almost into my face, and then sinks backwards onto the bed. The figure now rises above me, gives me a smile and a sly sideways glance before it sinks backwards, and falls against the wardrobe, where it comes to rest. Oh my goodness, I think to myself, this must be my only help, this must be her husband. I had better try to get some sense out of him as nothing is ready for the delivery, so I call out as I step towards him, 'Mr Copperopolis? I am pleased to see you. I think that your wife will have the baby very shortly so we had better get some things ready.'

He pushes himself from the wardrobe and stands over me; he is not a young man but he is very well built, and he looks quite fit even though he obviously imbibes freely. His wife's voice calls out again, and without looking at me he leaves the room. I stand, uncertain as to where my only help has gone. I ask myself if I should follow him as I will need his help. Mrs Copperopolis calls out, and I return to her. I cannot locate the baby's head in the pelvis, and the heart can be best located quite high in the abdomen. I need the gas and air machine, and I need to examine Mrs Copperopolis; I must have her husband's help. He enters the room wearing a large dark overcoat, and carrying a huge steaming black kettle. Putting the kettle down he leans on the wardrobe again. I can only think that he has put his coat on because the room is so cold, but at least I have some hot water. I speak to Mrs Copperopolis but it is Mr Copperopolis who responds and, as I step into the dark hall, I hear my bicycle crashing its way through the door.

Mrs Copperopolis gasps at the gas and air and, now gowned ready for the delivery, I make my first examination. The cervix is almost fully dilated but I cannot feel the hard vertex of the baby's head, only the bulging membranes. Then the membranes rupture, water runs down my gloved hand, and something small and firm lies between my fingers. For a moment I am unable to identify what I hold. I roll it between my fingers, and then I recognise it, it is a foot, the baby is being born in breech presentation. I withdraw my hand quickly, feeling almost as if I have been stung, then I realise that Mrs Copperopolis' eyes rest on me and her voice holds that quiet panic which every mother's holds when she enquires about her baby.

'Is the baby all right, nurse?'

8.40 p.m.

Taking a deep breath in order to control myself, I reply, 'Yes, Mrs Copperopolis, everything seems to be fine, but your baby has chosen to be born feet first. Did you know that it lay this way? Have you been to the doctor, didn't he say anything?'

But Mrs Copperopolis has no time to reply; the next contraction arrives, and along with it comes a tiny pink foot.

'Breathe the gas, Mrs Copperopolis, and don't push,' I hear myself almost shouting as I frantically look around for some way of raising her feet and of directing her pelvis towards me so that I can get near to the baby and control the birth of its head.

The wash basin stand on which I have laid out my instruments is behind me. Turning sideways, I grasp its marble top, and pull it nearer to the bed. It moves little but the feet make a tremendous noise as they scrape across the wooden floor. I gasp for breath as I look back at Mrs Copperopolis. Now both of the baby's feet are showing. The figure appears again; like Marley's ghost, it stands at the end of the bed, and I shout, probably louder than I need to, 'Mr Copperopolis, please help me to move this furniture.'

I had managed to move the wash basin stand. The figure, still draped in its black coat, moves slowly towards me as I shout out, 'Mr Copperopolis, will you please push the dressing table over towards the bed.'

For a moment he stands and looks at me, his dark hooded eyes meeting mine as I stare at him over my mask. Then the dressing table starts to move and, with a horrendous scraping sound, the large, dark piece of furniture heads towards me. It comes so fast that I am almost trapped between it and the wash basin, I scream out just in time.

'Stop, stop pushing, Mr Copperopolis.'

Fortunate for me his response is faster this time, and the dressing table comes to rest just inches from my hip and a little way from the side of the bed. Now I must turn Mrs Copperopolis around on the bed so that her pelvis is facing me. I look up. The figure is heading for the door, I must stop him before he disappears again. I shout out, 'Mr Copperopolis, could you please help your wife? I want her to turn around in the bed.'

He continues on out of the door, but as I lean over the large body of his wife, and attempt to get her to turn across the bed he reappears and leans over her. I would have had little need to give her an anaesthetic, had I have needed to, his breath would have done it for me. But mumbling some words to her, which I do not understand, he lifts her shoulders with ease, and she turns in the bed. Kissing her forehead as he places a pillow beneath her head, he is gone.

8.55 p.m.

The baby's body lies across my right hand as I slide three fingers of my left hand across its chest to find the neck. The chin should be the next promontory; it had been when we had practised this procedure with the rag doll in the classroom. We had closed our eyes when we tried out the procedure on the doll, but a small peep had always been possible to reassure us that things were as they should be. Now no peeping is possible – it all depends on touch. The promontory is not there, I push my fingers in further, I feel nothing that I can recognise. I can feel my own heart beating fast against my throat. Mrs Copperopolis calls out, and I feel pressure on my hand. I look up saying, 'Don't push, Mrs Copperopolis, use the gas, pant, pant as hard as you can.'

The pressure lessens, and I slide one finger a little to the left. The promontory is there, just a little ridge, but above it I find the small orifice I seek. Putting my finger in what I hope is the baby's mouth I press gently down. In the classroom the tutor had turned the head; here the mother, the baby and nature do it in unison. All I feel is the head turning to fill my right hand, and as Mrs Copperopolis calls out with her exertion; the baby comes out into the world with my finger in his mouth. With one foot on the hand basin and one foot on the dressing table, Mrs Copperopolis is delivered of a son. I exhale a long shuddering breath. I think the baby and I take our first breath in unison.

9.05 p.m.

As in the classroom, the head came through the pelvis once the narrowest dimension had been presented. He needs a little rubbing to wake him up, but he is soon wrapped in a towel, and is encased in his mother's warm and welcoming arms.

I stand surrounded by heavy furniture. I have no way to escape, and at the moment I feel that my legs are going to give way under me. I have carried out the delivery while standing on one knee at the bedside, and now my legs hurt as I stand, trapped. Mr Copperopolis has disappeared again. I don't know whether to feel angry or frightened, and I am just going to scream out his name again when I hear a voice. It is a voice which I am overjoyed to hear. Mrs O'Reilly walks into the room.

The baby looks pink and warm in his mother's arms. Although he has suffered a good deal of moulding, and he has a long thin head and some bruising around the chin, he responds well to all stimuli and even attempts to feed. He is quite small and weighs in at just over five pounds. Mrs O'Reilly says that he was fortunate, if he had weighed a few ounces more he might not have made it so easily, even through those hips. Mr Copperopolis sobers up considerably after Mrs O'Reilly's arrival. An electric fire is found, and the furniture is restored to its proper place.

10.30 p.m.

I am completing the notes, and I ask Mrs Copperopolis if she has her antenatal card available. It is found. There are few recordings on it, but I notice that Mrs Quinn had written Mrs O'Reilly's name down as midwife. Mrs O'Reilly studies the card as she asks, 'Why didn't you go to see your doctor, Mrs Copperopolis?'

I had not heard Mr Copperopolis speak before, now, with a deep throaty voice he almost shouts, 'Chance would have been a fine thing, we haven't had a doctor around here for a year, and the only hospital is miles away in the centre of town. We have to go it alone.'

Mrs O'Reilly looks up from the baby, which now lies in a small wooden crib at the end of the bed and is well within the small circle of warmth given off by the one-bar electric fire.

'Well I hope that you can keep off the brandy bottle, Mr Copperopolis, and look after these two for a few days. I will find a doctor to come in and see the baby tomorrow, and if you have any worries tonight you just ring Nurse Compton, it's the same number you rang me on.'

11.00 p.m.

He wheels my bike out of the house. An elderly lady comes down the stairs, he says something in Greek and she claps her hands over her head as she heads towards the bedroom. I hear an older child cry in the rooms above; the old lady hesitates momentarily, but does not stop.

'Thank you for your help and thank you for ringing Mrs O'Reilly, how did you know to ring her?' I speak as I climb onto the bike in the dark road. His smile is now genuine and, as he bends to kiss my cheek, the smell is of peppermint as he speaks, 'When I ring, you say that you are Pupil Midwife, I know who a pupil is, I have many who learn music. I have also seen that the midwife, the mistress of the class, is named Mrs O'Reilly. When the baby is arriving the wrong way around I think that maybe it is time for this pupil to have the guidance of the impresario. But I thank you for my son.'

I look back at him as I ride away, maybe I had him wrong, he had done everything that was needed of him, he had just done it in his own way. What a shame he drank so much.

17

Saturday 21st April

9.00 a.m.

It has been a busy week; only one delivery, but many home visits and clinics. The Macaronis twins are both doing well, despite all the attention they are getting from their various relatives. As my mother says, you can die from not having enough love, but few people die from too much of it. The Macaronis twins are certainly doing well on it. Mrs O'Reilly and I aren't doing too badly either, a bunch of flowers arrived from the maternal grandmother only yesterday – she has only just managed to get over from Italy, and she sent the flowers almost as her first act after holding both her grandsons, of course. Every time I visit I return with some delicacy to eat, or a bottle of wine. Mrs O'Reilly says that I will have to sign them off soon as she is becoming too used to having good wine with her dinner. The good life should end early next week when I enter them into my Case Book as case number five.

Now I lie in bed and stretch, today is my day off and I can forget all about it today. I have even decided not to swot today, and as I look out of the window I decide that this might be a good idea as, at last, the spring sun is shining. I leap back into the warm bed and pull the blankets up, but then the only cloud on my horizon comes into view. I had been looking forward to tonight's party, but after the events on the tennis court I am not so sure. I pull a blanket over my head, and look at the light shining through it. I had always avoided doctors, I had found them to be insincere and egotistical. Not that I had had a doctor as a boyfriend before, Tony is the first, but a friend in general training had supposedly been engaged to one of the housemen, that is until she became pregnant, then he didn't want to know her. She left the hospital, had a lovely baby boy, but never finished her training. He just carried on as if nothing had happened. That was how I saw things anyway. Now that Tony is showing his colours, do I really want to go to this party? Do I want to be with someone who is ashamed to be seen with me when he is with his associates? Do I want to be what he wants me to be, or do I want to be who I want to be? A shaft of sunlight hits the blanket and shines through to my face, and for some reason I see Alan Bunting, and I remember who I am. I shout out to myself as I jump out of bed.

'To hell with him, I'll get dressed up, and go knock him dead.'

7.00 p.m.

I know the road where Tony lives, it is one of the main roads that run beside the large hospital complex, but I am not sure exactly where the house is. I had got off the bus at what I guessed might be about the right place, but now as I cross the road, and look at the numbers on the large houses which fringe the road, I realise that I should have stayed on the bus for another stop. As I cross the road cars stop for me, and a young man leans out of one of the windows and whistles at me, another man forgets to start off as he watches me step onto the pavement, and the driver of the car behind beeps. I turn around and look and the man blows me a kiss. My confidence is raised by all this attention and I step out with increased assurance in the direction of Tony's lodgings.

I have dressed with considerable care this evening, in fact it has taken me most of the day to get ready. I had tried to do some reading, but the sun shining on the window, and the constant thought that I had to look good tonight, prevented the words of knowledge from penetrating further than my eyes. By mid-morning I had surrendered and the shops had soon gained my full attention. I could not decide what to wear, and had spent more than I intended to on a skirt with a daring split up its back. I knew that I had good legs; years of cycling in the hills of Derbyshire had seen to this. The lady in the shop said that the skirt looked great, however when I got it home the only blouse that would go with it was not very smart and it was also a couple of years old and dated. I had contemplated buying a new top, but when I had returned to the shops my attention had been drawn to some rather expensive and very elegant perfume.

My final choice of dress, from my less than extensive wardrobe, had been a dark green jersey wool dress. With its loose cowl collar, and its clinging body, it always looks chic, but I rarely wear it as I don't see myself as the chic type. I had bought it at a sale when I worked for a year as a staff nurse; I felt I had money to spare then. Now, as I walk down the road with my red high heels clicking, I am faintly embarrassed by the attention which I draw from the male car drivers. Possibly my Presbyterian upbringing and my Jewish mother are reason for my present predicament.

7.15 p.m.

The front door is open and two young men step through it; this is the correct house number, so I turn in at its broken gate. The young men ignore me as they squeeze past me at the gate but one of them turns around and calls to me, 'Party's on the ground floor'.

I nod my thanks, and head through the door. The inside of the house seems dark after the brightness of the street, and at first I can't see where I am, but I can hear the noise. I am standing in a large hallway with a high ceiling. The architecture looks similar to that which I have seen in houses on the other side of town, but there the halls were decaying from neglect; here the hall is furnished. An old patterned carpet covers much of the floor, deep chairs lie around its sides, and a rumpled sofa just peeps out from under the stairs. The light comes from a leaded window on the far wall and through a door that stands open to my right. About thirty young people mill around in the space with glasses and voices raised. I had expected to be one of the early birds but it seems that many have arrived before me. I stand unsure of where I should go, and then I see Tony. He stands with a group of young men by a low table in the middle of the hall. I recognise a couple of the men from my visits to the Students Union bar, and as I walk towards them one of the young men touches Tony's shoulder and points towards me.

8.00 p.m.

I stand in a different part of the hall, but now I have a long-stemmed glass in my hand and I am sipping a rum and pep. The formalities are over, I have been introduced to a couple of his fellow students and Tony went off to fetch himself another beer about ten minutes ago. A large armchair stands empty by the stairs, I drift towards it and lower myself into its soft and supportive arms. The rum has made me feel a little more relaxed, and I take time to review my situation. Suddenly, through the noise, I hear a voice I know well, it is only there for a second and then it is gone. I look up at the stairs which rise above and almost in front of me. A long skirt topping string sandals appears in the stairwell, and I look with amazement as Maureen's head and shoulders follow them. She does not see me; her animated and smiling face is turned upwards towards the person who is following her. A tall slim figure in a pale grey pinstriped suit follows her, and I gaze in amazement as I see the suited figure, now standing on the bottom step, take Maureen's shoulders, and turn her towards the open door at the bottom of the stairs. Still maintaining the hold, the suited figure follows Maureen through the open doorway, her high heeled shoes clicking on the tiles.

Tony's voice speaks above me, 'Come on, let's go and dance. They're putting some music on in the other room.'

The end of the sentence is almost lost as Bill Haley booms out from the unseen room. We have rocked and we have rolled, I have imbibed two more rums. We are now smooching around the floor as Nat King Cole tells us that we are 'Unforgettable'. Tony's hand has strayed down to my buttocks three times, I have removed it twice, but now the rum has taken over – I think the dregs at the bottom of the bottle must have been extra potent. We are now passing the bean bags, which are piled up in the corner of the room. As we turn around I get a quick glimpse of Maureen; she lies back across the bean bags with her eyes closed and her mouth open. As we turn further I see the suited lady, now in cream silk sleeves, drop peanuts into Maureen's mouth, they are both laughing, totally involved in each other.

'Who is the woman in the grey suit?' I ask as we slide cross the floor away from them. Tony looks at me for a moment and then he asks, 'What woman?'

I nod my head sideways.

'The one sitting next to the bean bags.'

He raises his head and looks over my head, 'Oh! That's the senior house officer, it's her party that we are at. She's got a reg's post somewhere up north, she will be off next week, she's pretty bright, should go places.'

'Does she live in this house?'

'Oh no, we are just using this house because it has the largest hall, only medical students live here. Anyway, why are we talking about her when you are looking particularly good this evening?'

He pulls me to him as Nat starts singing, 'Walking my baby back home'.

I murmur, 'Thank you, kind sir,' into his pale blue shirt front as we circle around the centre of the stone clad floor, our faces close and our bodies pressing. He murmurs into my hair 'You smell gorgeous.' I am about to thank Guerlain, but the moment is mine so I take it.

Nat is telling me once again that I am 'Unforgettable'. We stand in the centre of the floor hardly moving, so closely packed that only the slightest movement of the feet is possible. In a husky voice he asks, 'Shall we go upstairs?'

We pass others coming down as we climb the stairs, hesitating to kiss as we squeeze past them. The climb takes time. At the top heavy doors open from a landing and the stairs continue on upwards.

We fall towards one of the doors laughing as we go, and taking one hand from my waist Tony opens the door, and we fall in through it. A dressing table mirror reflects the room, the light over it the only illumination in the room. In the dim far end of the room I see a large bed piled high with coats. Kicking the door closed behind him Tony seizes me, and in a passionate embrace we fall backwards across the room. Pushing coats aside we land on the edge of the bed. The cowl collar of my dress frustrates him but the tight woollen skirt has ridden up to my thigh, and his eager hand soon finds the top of my leg where the stocking ends and the lace begins. I can feel him hard against my other thigh, and my brain is telling me to call a halt before we go too far, but I feel mellow after the rum and the smell of Tony is intoxicating.

Cold air passes over me. He is gone; the hand has gone; the pressure has gone; the moment has gone. He is standing beside the bed with his back towards me. His voice is dry and hard, and it catches as he speaks, 'Oh no, you're not catching me like that. I know what you're up to, you get all tarted up and I get excited, then we have sex, you say that you are pregnant, and then I have to marry you. Well not this one, my sweet, this one doesn't get caught like that.'

He swings around, and I see myself lying on the bed with my dress almost up to my waist, and my silly new lace knickers pulled sideways. He puts his hand out to help me, I refuse it, and in one move I swing my legs over, stand and straighten my dress. I cannot think, my mind has gone dead, this is the situation I had tried so hard to prevent. I have no right of reply, he holds all the high ground, doctors always make sure that they hold that. I do not look at him, but sliding across to the mirror I drag my hand across my hair and run my finger around my lips. He allows me no leverage, and before I turn I see him in the mirror, he stands with the door open and his back to me. I am going to cry, I feel so ashamed, although ashamed of what I'm not sure. Gaining control of myself I head to the door as he lets it go. I know he intends to descend the stairs with his head held high; I must follow alone, in this way he can give the impression that he has taken all he wants and has discarded the rest. However, during my midwifery rounds I have been to a brothel a few times, and I have learnt a few tricks of the trade. The long-legged madam, with her high heeled shoes and high-piled hair, did not let her clients control the situation, she gave them the amount of attention they had paid for, and she always saw them from her premises; she had the last word. Now I am very sober. I reach the door before it closes, and as Tony begins to descend the stairs I place my hands on his shoulders, and with chin up I stand behind him. He looks up at me with surprise in his face, I smile down at him and, as he hesitates, I swing past him. Maureen gives me the first eye contact of the evening as I thank her companion for a lovely evening, and head for the door.

11.00 p.m.

My heart had been beating fast as I left the house, and I had not felt the cool wind. My adrenaline had been flowing too fast, but now as I stand at the bus stop the light wool dress does little to keep me warm. Several young men arrive at the bus stop; they push each other around and leer at me, one asks me where I am going; another answers for me.

'She is going to sell it at one of the big hotels in town.'

Raucous laughter follows. I keep my back to them and my eyes firmly in front. Maybe I had dressed up like a tart, maybe Tony was right. The bus arrives and the young men squeeze past me and rush up the stairs calling to each other as they go. I make my way along the almost empty bus and take a seat at the front, behind the driver. The conductor, a tall West Indian man, swings his way along the bus, his ticket punch machine held at chest height in front of him. He sings to himself as he comes, and his voice seems to continue with the tune as he asks, 'Where to, madam?'

I tell him the stop I want, he dispenses the ticket and then, raising his large brown eyes upwards, he says, 'I'll make sure that rowdy lot stay up there and leave you in peace, madam, don't know how to behave, young men these days.'

I smile my thanks and almost burst out laughing. I look at my reflection in the window.

Well now I know where I stand with him, can't say I'm keen enough to make any more effort, so goodbye, Tony.

The dark reflection looks back at me but does not reply, I hear the conductor come back down the stairs. I had better stop talking to myself before he thinks that I am a bit odd after all.

18

Sunday 22nd April

8.00 a.m.

I wake with a start. The events of last night flood back into my brain. Suddenly I feel quite light at heart, Tony really was not my cup of tea, and now I think about it in the light of day I have to admit that my lessons at the brothel had come in very useful. I feel free and myself again, Tony's behaviour has made the decision for me, I won't ever see him again. But what about Maureen, what was she playing at? Mrs O'Reilly's head appears around the door.

'Thought I heard you moving, do you want a cup of tea?'

Swinging my legs out of bed, I grab for the dressing-gown; yesterday evening, when all my attention had been on making myself glamorous, it had been thrown on the floor.

'No, thank you very much for the offer, but I think I'll get up.'

She is sitting in her usual place by the kitchen table, and as usual the newspaper is in front of her face. I can see the clean stiff starched grey of her uniform as it covers her legs. She is on duty today and I have another day off, but I know that she will call me if a delivery comes up and I will be there like a shot. The teapot is pushed across the table, and her voice comes from behind the paper.

'Did you have a good night then?'

My hesitation is enough to lift her eyes over the top of the large sheets of the newspaper. The all-seeing eyes look at me over the top of her glasses. Avoiding her gaze, I grasp the handle of the teapot and pull a cup towards me.

'Oh, as good as that was it?'

She returns to her newspaper, I pour tea.

I speak to the now only just warm, brown, fluid, 'Tony was in a mood, I don't think I'll see him again. Well he wasn't really in a mood, but he's so fond of himself there really isn't much room for anyone else.'

The paper rustles as pages turn.

'There are a few of those around believe me, but you are right, they are best avoided.'

Silence falls as I try to sip the half-cold tea; I give up and speak instead.

'Maureen was there.'

The paper rustles again.

'You mean that friend of yours, well that sort of friend. Who was she with?'

I hesitate again, and then pick my words with care.

'She was with the Senior House Officer who has got a Registrar's post up North, it was her leaving party. They say that she is very clever, and it won't be long before she makes consultant.'

The paper has now been lowered, and Mrs O'Reilly looks me full in the face as she speaks, 'Well that answers it all doesn't it? I presume you mean that they were together in the carnal sense.'

I don't really know what to say so I just mumble, 'Well yes, they were very friendly . . .'

She rises, folds the newspaper and throws it across the table towards me. She walks down the side of the table and heads for the door as she speaks.

'No wonder she got rid of your boyfriends, fancied you herself didn't she?'

I hear her chuckling to herself as she descends the stairs, and as she closes the clinical room door I am left sitting in silence with that impossible idea reverberating through my brain. The events of last night now seem even worse, and as I churn over my long relationship with Maureen I begin to imagine things that probably never even happened. I make fresh tea and some toast.

Mrs O'Reilly returns to the kitchen now wearing her outdoor coat and her grey hat adorned with its midwifery badge.

'Are you staying in this morning?'

Not wanting to spray her in toast crumbs I nod my affirmative reply. She pulls on driving gloves as she replies, 'OK, I'll leave the phone with you, if it's very urgent you know the houses I will be at, I will only be an hour or so anyway.'

She turns to leave and then changes her mind, and looks back at me.

'Don't look so worried, you don't have to marry her, not unless you want to of course.'

This time she does turn, and I hear her laughing to herself as she descends the stairs.

11.30 a.m.

Books and notes are spread out in front of me as I sit cross-legged on my bed; the final exam is in four weeks. I have looked at my Case Book, and from my notes I have reminded myself of the cases recorded in it. Baby Waller is doing fine; it is his parents who have taken all my time. I have managed to convince Mr Waller that he should clear the small second bedroom of all its rubbish, and introduce his eldest child to a new separate lifestyle. I even spent a couple of hours one morning helping him take down the stairs such bulky items as an old double mattress. It was time well spent for, on my next visit, the large cot had gone and there was room to move in the main bedroom. I have rung the Council and have asked them to please collect the extra rubbish from the Waller's front garden before it becomes a garden feature; several gardens in the row do have such features. I will however have to check the state of my kidneys before I can offer any more help as any delay in my leaving the Waller's premises brings forth another cup of tea, and another, and another. I had a good chat with Mrs Waller while Mr Waller was at the factory collecting his money. She has promised that she will visit her GP, and will ask about having a coil fitted. Their house can just about hold two children, and Mr Waller will be lost if Mrs Waller has more children – well any more at the moment, anyway.

I close the Case Book, and now my mind comes back to Maureen, I decide that I can do nothing but draw a line under the whole thing. After the exams we will all be going our different ways, so what does it matter? I try to focus my attention on a midwifery book when the phone rings. I wait to see if Mrs O'Reilly will answer it, but I have not heard her return and the phone continues to ring.

12.05 p.m.

'Midwife's house, Pupil Midwife Compton speaking, can I help you?'

There is silence and then I hear a rustling sound and a voice speaks, but it is not speaking to me, I try again.

'Hello, the midwife speaking, can I help . . . ?'

Before I can finish the sentence a voice booms out in a strong Irish accent, 'Will you tell the midwife that Mary, er, um, Mrs Maloney is having the babby.'

The voice speaks to someone else, and then the line goes dead. I wait for a moment to see if the person will speak to me again, but now I am used to this type of communication, and I know exactly who is in labour.

I nip into the kitchen and into the sitting room. Mrs O'Reilly is not there. So, returning to my room, I take a clean starched uniform out of the wardrobe, and, pulling on the thirty denier stockings, I head down the stairs. I am at the bottom of the second flight of stairs, gas and air machine and delivery bag in tow, when Mrs O'Reilly's face appears round Mrs Stone's kitchen door. She beckons me to stop as she drains the last dregs from a cup. Returning the cup to the kitchen, she asks, 'Thought I heard the phone, who is it?'

She stands beside me dabbing at her lips with a handkerchief. I drop the gas and air machine to the floor as I reply.

'It's Mrs Maloney, you know, the woman at the . . .'

I search for the right words, but she needs no more and, picking up the discarded box, she leads the way to the outside door.

'I'll come with you on this one; I think that baby might need a bit of support.'

She calls back to me as I head for the bike, 'Leave that, we can go in the car.'

The day is bright and the sun warm, just my luck I think; on wet, cold nights I get to ride the bike. Mrs O'Reilly is speaking as she pulls on her gloves, and gets into the black Austin Seven, which is parked at the kerb.

'We have no idea what her dates are, have we? You've seen her couple of times; I think that you have said the baby is small,' says Mrs O'Reilly.

I am looking around at the weather and the daffodils, and I am not really listening to her. The car door on the pavement side opens and the voice shouts, 'Well get in before we're too late.'

I hurry across the pavement and, bending my knees, I

slide into the front seat beside her, the delivery bag on my knee almost touching the windscreen. We set off on the now familiar route with me acting as guide.

'I hope you've got the notes.'

She doesn't wait for a reply but continues, 'Remind me.'

I start to read from the notes but she stops me.

'I know that, I do read the notes regularly, tell me more about her situation, does she live in that room at the top of the house, or is that just her place of business?'

She looks sideways for traffic as we join the main road, and we set off as if from a pit stop at Brands Hatch. Regaining my hat and my head, I speak.

'She has always been at that address when I visited.'

She looks sideways at me her lips tight.

'You mean you have never asked her. Did you get an address from the person who rang?'

Without waiting for my reply, she answers herself.

'No, well let's just hope that someone knows where she is, and that we can get there before this baby is born.'

I sit with my hands clasped tightly around the handle of the delivery bag. I had felt so confident, I knew who had rung and I thought I knew where to find her. But in all my zeal and excitement at being in a brothel I had forgotten to treat Mrs Maloney with the courtesy and professionalism that a patient deserves. I had not seen her as a pregnant woman who deserved all my attention; I had been distracted by her environment. Both Mrs O'Reilly and I had asked her to go into hospital to have the baby, but she had refused. In fact, I had been unable to find her after I had made my last attempt to get her to go to hospital; I had only found her again last week. We draw up at the door, and I am relieved to see the tall lady standing in the open doorway, she will know where Mrs Maloney is; my incompetence may not be fatal. The woman looks out of place; high heeled shoes, floral dressing-gown, red lips, and blue ringed eyes look incongruous in this dirty sunlit street. Several people adorn the pavement by the door, and women stand at the other side of the road, their folded arms proclaim their disdain, and their ill-wagging chins cannot stop as they take pleasure in this moment. I see Mrs O'Reilly's head appear above the car, she faces her audience, and I hear her voice controlled and controlling as, with chin high, she speaks, 'Good morning ladies, a fine morning, isn't it?'

The women mumble and, lowering their arms, they move along the pavement to regroup just yards further on. Mrs O'Reilly walks around the car, and those standing on the pavement disperse; now it is my turn to receive her gaze.

'This is your case, Nurse Compton. I hope we're not going to stand out here on the pavement putting on a show all day.'

The tall lady has retreated into the house, and I am very relieved to see that she is inviting us to come in. Mrs Maloney must be upstairs.

12.20 p.m.

The room looks dull and rather dirty. Heavy curtains are pulled back over grey coloured nets. What light does enter the room reveals little charm. But I have no time to admire the room; Mrs Maloney is in the late stage of labour. She appears to be in a good deal of stress as she hangs onto the bedstead and sweats profusely. I take the gas and air machine from the tall lady; she has just entered the room, and her bright red face tells me that she did not enjoy climbing the two flights of stairs. Putting the mask on, I tell Mrs Maloney to breathe in and blow out. Mrs O'Reilly listens to the baby's heart, looks at me, and raises her eyes to the ceiling, and, as I peel myself out of my coat, I call out, 'Can we have some hot water?'

Dropping my coat in the corner, I turn back to the bed. The water arrives; it is carried in the hands of a woman who looks even younger than my patient. Now I am gowned and gloved and, with my equipment ready, I commence my examination of Mrs Maloney. I have hardly started when she screams and raises her buttocks from the bed. I stop all movement and wait for her to calm down. I hear Mrs O'Reilly as she encourages her to breath in the gas.

'What is it, what can you feel?' Mrs O'Reilly's voice is urgent.

I nod my head to say nothing, the muscles relax and I try again. She does not scream, the gas and air machine rattles hard but the muscles tighten again, and then I see a stain of blood on the dressing towel and the trickle of blood starts. I call Mrs O'Reilly's attention to it, she glances over and in a quiet voice asks, 'Placenta previa?'

Now I feel the cervix, and the young woman shouts out, the membranes have ruptured and the baby's head is there, it should be born quite soon. I report my finding as I wash my hands.

'There is a good deal of blood, but the head is coming down; I don't think that it is the placenta and if it is it's too late to do anything.'

Mrs O'Reilly stands at the bottom of the bed and looks at the young woman as she starts to speak.

'Then it must be, hum, what do you think it could be, Nurse Compton?'

She chooses to test my knowledge at this precise moment! I drag the backwaters of my mind, and come up with one of my tutor's sayings, 'Well, if it's not internal, it must be external.'

Then the truth hits me, can it be a torn vagina? But the baby hasn't been born yet. I voice my doubts, 'It can't be a vaginal tear; the baby hasn't come through yet.'

Mrs O'Reilly pulls her mouth sideways as she looks at me over her glasses.

'It seems that the sex act isn't enough for some of the masochistic devils who are around these days. I think that she must have been going up town to get a bit more money.'

At that point Mrs Maloney screams and shouts out, 'I must push.' My attention must be returned to the present; what happened in the past can be discussed later.

12.45 p.m.

The baby comes very quickly. She is covered in blood; she is very small and she is very still. Speedily I separate her from her mother, lay her face down on my hand and suck out her mouth, she does not move. Mrs O'Reilly stands by me.

'Blow in her face.'

She speaks quietly as she looks down on the pale flaccid body. I blow gently. Momentarily the tiny face screws up and the little fingers twitch.

Mrs O'Reilly's voice sounds above me, 'I'll get an ambulance, these two need some time in hospital.'

1.20 p.m.

The audience on the street stands in silence as the ambulance doors close. I sit on a stool beside Mrs Maloney; she has her face turned from me as she looks at the wall of the ambulance. The baby lies in her Perspex bubble at my other side. Mrs Maloney has not looked at her daughter nor has she asked what sex her child is. I have told her that she has a daughter, and the ambulance men have referred to her in the female gender when they were handling her, but her mother has not looked at her.

Mrs Maloney had not been happy when we told her that she had to go to hospital. I had found a nightdress in a drawer, it lay, along with some discoloured old knickers and a bra, discarded and forgotten, part of another world. One of the other girls had lent her a toilet bag, which now holds part of a used tablet of soap, a flannel and a comb. I look across at her, the brightly coloured hair, still stiff from its last application of hair spray, now lies squashed and malformed at the side of her head. Her eyes, still blue from the make-up around them, are now, like much of her face, swollen and red. But now that much of the make-up is gone she looks young. I look down at her notes which lie on my lap; they tell me that she is two years younger than me. We are from the same age group, and probably from almost the same background, but what different lives we have led. I try to talk to her.

'Have you decided what name your baby will have?'

She does not speak but turns further away from me.

'What's your name?'

I look down at the notes.

'Mary, that would be a nice name for her.'

The voice sounds croaked at first.

'She can join the rest of the women in our bloody family then, can't she?'

Now she turns a little towards me as she clears her throat. 'Every female in our family is called Mary, Mary this, Mary that, Mary the other.'

'Well you could pick another name, and you could get her baptised before your family have a chance to have a say in it.'

Now she looks me in the face, her eyes are green, and she has a pretty face.

'I suppose I could, but what sort of name? My mother would just stick Mary on the end of whatever I call her.'

'Well, what name do you like? You could give her two names yourself if you want.'

Now she giggles as she raises herself upon one elbow, and for the first time looks at her daughter.

'I like Naomi, I call myself that sometimes, she could be my Naomi couldn't she?'

Now she blushes.

'Not that I'd let any of those evil sods lay a finger on her.'

She scowls across at the baby, I must try to get her into a positive mood.

'You can give her another name that goes with Naomi, something like, say, Ann.'

Now she is quite animated; she leans over and touches the side of the Perspex bubble with her scarlet finger tips.

'She can be my Naomi Ann, but my mother will still put Mary at the end of it.'

Her eyes catch mine, and I see the idea hit her.

'What's your name, nurse?'

Now it's my turn to look down at the notes.

'It's Dorothy, but . . .'

The ambulance doors fly open, and as they wheel the baby out, her mother calls after her, 'Bye Naomi Ann Dorothy, I'll see you in a little while, me and you have got things to talk about.'

2.30 p.m.

Mrs Maloney lies on the smooth white sheet; her night-dress looks grey against it. A young doctor is examining her, and she winces in agony.

'My God, what a mess.'

He pull off the glove and looks at the nurse who stands beside him.

'Who may I ask delivered her? How did she get in this mess?'

I cough to attract his attention.

'I delivered her, um, I delivered her at her home.'

He looks at me in silence as he takes the notes from the nurse. I continue, 'Um, it was a rapid delivery . . .'

He continues speaking for me, 'Of a rather small baby I see. Who, may I ask, are you?

He flicks through the notes.

'Did they call you in from the street, or are you her next door neighbour? Whoever you are do not try delivering any more babies. Oh, a pupil midwife I see, well I hope you never come to work at this hospital.'

Giving me a hard stare he heads for the gap in the curtains.

'We'll get her down to theatre, nurse. I'd like to look at her properly, I can't deal with that in a bed.'

Mrs Maloney's eyes meet mine, she opens her mouth to speak, and I shake my head, the doctor and nurse leave.

3.15 p.m.

I look through the window, baby Naomi Ann lays still and pale in her incubator. She does not have any tubes inserted, so she can't be too bad, I think she should make it. Tears sting the back of my eyes and my throat feels heavy. I have never been reprimanded in such a way before, but what could I say? Could I shout out, it wasn't me who tore her vagina, it was some male pervert who paid her for the privilege of doing it? The dark outline of a sad face looks back at me.

Mrs Maloney has been to theatre, she lays in bed pale against her white pillow as she sleeps. The nurse, who can hardly look me in the face, tells me that they will be keeping her in hospital for a few days. I thank her for the information and leave. Then I realise I have no way of getting home, I have no money for the bus, and my bike is at home. I ring Mrs O'Reilly's number and ask if they will reverse the call. With relief I hear Mrs O'Reilly's voice, 'Wait there, I'll come down. What is the matter? Has the baby died?'

I try to sound cheery, 'No everything is fine, they are . . .'

She interrupts me.

'You can tell me when I get there, you're at the General Hospital, I presume.'

4.20 p.m.

We stand by the glass and look across at the baby; as if to reassure us, she raises one of her hands half an inch from the mattress. Mrs O'Reilly touches my arm.

'Looks like she is going to make it.'

I look at the baby as I grip my bottom lip between my teeth.

'Yes it looks as though baby Naomi Ann is going to be all right.'

'Oh, got a name has she, seems she'll be all right in every sense, how did that come about?'

I screw my face up and nod my head sideways, the tears are near, and I fight to hold them. But Mrs O'Reilly has been around too long; such tears don't need to be shed to be seen.

'What happened?'

She speaks as she turns away from the window. Now the tears will not be held, they roll.

'I think I saw directions to a canteen down that corridor, let's see if we can get a cup of tea. Must be hours since you last ate anything.'

We have convinced the tea ladies that we are nurses in need of a drink, and the tea and a slice of bread and jam have been found. The story has been told, or should I say the case history has been completed. Mrs O'Reilly looks at me in silence for some moments before she speaks.

'Well you can't go carrying that on your own, now can you? You could have said that I was present at the delivery.'

I grimace as I reply, 'I didn't get time.'

The high ground had been taken once again, but it is no good me trying to explain that. I look at Mrs O'Reilly, and for the first time since I had walked into the hospital I smile, I know that I don't have to explain about the high ground to this woman.

'Don't tell them what she does will you?' I say through the second half of the jam sandwich.

I look up at her, and smile as I say, 'I don't think I'll be applying for a job at this hospital.'

19

Monday 23rd April

9.00 a.m.

I ride my bicycle down to the General Hospital, which is situated almost in the centre of the city. The journey is not easy, there is a good deal of traffic, and I have to get off and walk a few times.

9.30 a.m.

With my bicycle left in the porter's charge, I head for the gynaecology ward. Mary is sitting up chatting to the lady in the next bed, and her face, now devoid of make-up, looks young, fresh and pretty. Having asked for permission to visit, I now walk towards her. She smiles and holds her hand high in greeting, and I raise mine in return as I speak, 'Good morning, Mary, how are you today?'

Her face tells all.

'Oh, I'm fine nurse and Naomi Ann is doing well. They have said that I might be able to go home tomorrow, but Naomi will have to stay here for a little while until she puts on some weight.'

She can't seem to stop talking, and now she swings her legs over the side of the bed and drops her feet to the floor. She winces as she rises but now her arms are swinging around as she fights her way into a hospital dressing-gown. She walks slowly and stiff legged over to the Ward Sister, who watches her approach over the top of her glasses. Their conversation is short, and in the blink of an eye she is waddling back towards me with a grin on her face.

'If you fetch one of those wheelchairs and take me up we can go to see Naomi now.'

I look across at the Sister, she smiles and nods her head. She had not been on duty yesterday when Mary came in. She seems to be very friendly and maybe she hasn't heard about my appalling midwifery. Who am I kidding? Of course she will have read the notes and taken report.

We are in the lift and on our way to the Midwifery Unit where Naomi Ann lies in the premature baby unit. We are alone in the lift, Mary speaks to the white clad wall, and I can just hear her.

'Told that doctor that it was my boyfriend that did that to me, I told him that it wasn't you.'

The lift doors open, and we fight our way through white coats and aprons as we leave for our destination. We arrive at the glass window, and she turns and faces me.

'I just told him that I had a rough boyfriend; he said was he that abusive? I just said, yes, he done it 'cause he didn't want the baby. I told him that I'm going away on my own when I get out and I'm taking the baby with me.'

She looks at me with tear-filled eyes which now look greener than ever.

'They won't take Naomi away, will they? I didn't tell 'em what I was doing, you won't tell 'em will you? 'Cause if you do they'll take her and put her in a home, then my Naomi will end up the same as me.'

Now the tears run down her face and a nurse who is passing stops to ask if we are all right.

'Yes thank you, just a little emotional after the birth, be better when she sees her baby.'

I smile with what I hope is my professional smile and

the nurse passes on. I put my arm around Mary's shoulders and she leans sideways and pours salty tears down my coat.

'You know, nurse, you are the first person who has been nice to me since I got to this country.'

I think now is probably the best time to raise some questions.

'Where are you going to live when you get out of hospital, Mary?'

She does not reply, but the tears stop.

'You can't really go back to your room, now can you? Maybe you can find some lodging near by.'

She interrupts me with a sudden cheerful note.

'I've got an aunt who lives in Bristol, maybe I can stay with her until I can get back over to Ireland.'

She looks up at me, a smile on her face.

'But how will you manage to get in to see Naomi, she might have to stay here for a week or two.'

I can't let her go wandering off. Firstly, if she leaves the baby behind she might never come back for her and, secondly, I need to keep my eye on her until the baby is ten days old. To be mercenary about this I can't afford to have a case disappear before my eyes.

'I can look in the paper and see if I can find something for you, but don't you be in a hurry to leave this hospital, give yourself a little rest.'

10.30 a.m.

I cycle back up the hill, I have stayed at the hospital longer than I intended. Baby Naomi is fine, she has weighed in at just over four pounds. She is breathing well and they are tube feeding her but they hope to start bottle feeding her tomorrow. Mary, that is Mrs Maloney, has been asked if she would like to breastfeed her. She showed some enthusiasm, and I am becoming more hopeful that she won't do a runner as soon as she gets out.

Mrs Stone greets me as I open the door. She speaks urgently in my face as I stand in the doorway, my bike hanging between two steps, 'Don't bring that in. Mrs O'Reilly has gone down to 45 Rose Gardens to a Mrs . . .'

'Grey.'

I complete the sentence for her as I turn the bike and, leaping on it almost before I am through the gate, I set off at speed. I have been to visit Mrs Grey several times over the last two weeks. According to her dates she should have given birth on or around April the 10th; she was to be one of my sure-fire certainties. Now, as soon as I am away from the phone, she goes into labour. It's her third baby, her other two children are only two years and one and a half years old respectively, and it is expected that this delivery will be normal, and fast.

10.40 a.m.

I know this estate now, and at full speed I whirl along Attlee Road and swing into Rose Gardens. This cul-de-sac, which lies on the edge of the large and still-growing council estate, might once have had roses in its centre, but any sign of a flowering plant has long ago been removed. Now a path runs across the flat piece of ground around which the semi-detached houses are arranged. This path continues on between two of the houses and disappears through a break in the wooden fence which runs around the backs of the houses.

A large lady waddles along this path carrying a bulging shopping bag. I have used the row of shops at the entrance to the cul-de-sac several times myself.

Flinging my leg over the seat, and hitting what remains of the gate with my bike, I run up the path to the side of the building. I know this dwelling contains the premises numbered 22 and 23, which are maisonettes. I know that Mrs Grey lives at Number 22 on the ground floor. I also know that Mrs Plumb lives at number 23 on the first floor.

The door is open by a tall thin woman who I know to be Mrs Plumb. Before she can speak I get my words out, 'Is the midwife here?'

I don't wait for an answer, I know Mrs Plumb, she is a bit slow on the uptake, it has, on previous occasions, taken me ten minutes to elicit an answer from her, even when the question was as simple as, 'Is Mrs Grey in?' It's not that she doesn't understand, or that what she says is wrong, it's just that it seems to take an age for words to soak into her head, and after you have seen the light dawn in her eyes it takes another eternity for her to find the words with which to reply.

Now I am in a hurry as I can hear Mrs O'Reilly's voice coming from behind the bedroom door.

10.55 a.m.

I have taken over the delivery. Mrs O'Reilly has handed over the case and now she puts on her driving gloves and heads out to her car. It's not safe to leave such things as a motorised vehicle, in fact any vehicle, at the side of the road for long on this estate; the children are supposed to be at school, but they always seem to appear when a car stops.

I listen to the baby's heart and make an examination. All is well and as I enter my findings in the notes which lie on a dressing table I am confident that this will be a normal delivery, and that it will take place before the morning is over. I sigh with contentment; number eleven is in the Case Book, straightforward and normal.

It is a normal delivery; the baby is born without any difficulty. It is a fine boy and Mrs Grey is delighted, she already has two girls who are at the moment staying with their grandmother. The baby is wiped, wrapped in a dressing towel and passed to his mother. Mrs Plumb hovers around cooing and babbling at the baby. She had done her job and the hot water came when needed. I write the appropriate times in the notes, and turn to wait for the arrival of the afterbirth.

12.30 p.m.

The afterbirth has not been delivered. I have given the prescribed amount of ergometrine, and now I encourage Mrs Grey to push. Nothing but a slow stream of blood arrives. I massage the fundus; it rises hard under my hand. I push it gently and, with an encouraging smile, I get Mrs Grey involved.

'Give me a nice big push now please, Mrs Grey.'

Much of her attention is directed towards Mrs Plumb who giggles and coos over the baby. She makes comments about the colour of his hair which she is convinced is red, and the colour of his eyes which she claims are blue. Mrs Grey becomes quite agitated by these acclamations, and almost climbs out of the bed to have a look for herself.

'There's nobody in our family with red hair,' she declares as I press her back to the bed.

I have an idea and call out to Mrs Plumb.

'Mrs Plumb, could you please bring the baby over, and give him to his mother? She wants to see what colour his hair is.'

I look across the room, Mrs Plumb is looking at me, her mouth is open, and her eyes are wide. I step across the room and lift the baby, she follows me. At last the words come, 'Oh, I couldn't have touched him, nurse.'

Now I remember Mrs Plumb does not have children, but I have more on my plate than to worry about than Mrs Plumb's infertility. The baby is with his mother, he has even tried to suck her nipple, but still the trickle of blood comes, but no afterbirth arrives. I look at the clock on the dresser; twenty minutes have passed since the birth, and still no afterbirth. Should I give more ergometrine and wait? Or should I send for Mrs O'Reilly's assistance? Mrs Grey turns her head sideways and coughs, a red mass appears in the bed. In my mind I cheer as I descend on the mass with gloved hands. A large clot of blood falls into the receptacles, and the trickle increases to a small flow. Now my alarm bells ring and, as I search in my bag for more ergometrine, I call over my shoulder, 'Mrs Plumb, could you please go to the telephone and call the midwife? Tell her that the afterbirth is not coming.'

I have injected the ergometrine and now I turn around. Mrs Plumb is still standing by the cot. Before I can say anything she says, 'No, I don't think that I could phone the midwife.'

I look at her in silent shock. What is she talking about? Then I realise that she has just answered my first request. I had asked it in the form of a question and that is how she has answered it. Grabbing her shoulders with my blood-stained gloves I spin her around and push her towards the door of the room. Stopping by my raincoat I delve into the pocket and pull out one of my precious shillings. She turns to protest as we reach the outer door but throwing it open I push her out and, pressing the shilling into her hand, I am just about to tell her what to do when she says, ' 'Cause I wouldn't know what to say if I phoned her.'

I stop in my tracks and look at her and, then I realise that she is just finishing off the sentence which she had started some time ago. Now I know that this is going to be hopeless, she can never make a phone call. In despair I look around. A large lady waddles down the road with her shopping bags.

'Hello! Hello! Can you help me?'

I shout as loud as I can but the woman continues on her way, seemingly oblivious of all around her. Now Mrs Plumb comes into her own, she may not be eloquent but she is fleet of foot as she dashes out of the gate, across the depleted rose garden, and with hand outstretched, accosts the good lady. After a short discourse, where all the words come from the large lady, I see them turn and look across at me. I wave, encouraging them to come in my direction. Reluctantly, the large figure starts to move towards the gate, and after giving them encouragement to continue in my direction, I dash into the bedroom, retrieve my pen from under my now bloody gown and scribble down Mrs O'Reilly's number along with the words, 'afterbirth won't come' on a piece of paper torn from the case notes. The large lady has just made it through the gate so I go to meet her, and I speak as I arrive in front of her.

'Thank you very much, madam.'

She looks me up and down but doesn't turn a hair, just asks, 'What's up nurse, having a bit of bother?'

I reply as calmly and quickly as I can.

'Just a little bit, nothing we can't handle, but I wondered if you could go, as quickly as you can, up to the phone and call this number for me.'

In a Scottish accent, she replies, 'That'll be no problem, nurse, but I don't know about the hurry bit, it's a wee way up to the phone box.'

My voice holds desperation as I say, 'Please try.'

She transfers the shopping bag from one hand to the other, and puffs loudly to emphasise its weight, and the immensity of the task which I give her. I watch her with some misgivings as she heads for the gate, her shuffling steps ponderous and stiff. She looks down at the blood-stained piece of paper which I have pushed into her hand, and blows air loudly through her lips again. Then she stops, and all lassitude vanishes as flinging the hand which holds the paper into the air she waves it like a flag, and in a high-pitched raucous voice calls out loud enough to waken the dead, 'Hey, Jimmy, come here, I need you.'

The youth is an ill-clad thirteen-year-old. He stops in mid-flight and looks across at her. He stands in the depleted rose garden uncertain as to whether he should risk this woman's wrath, and run for it, or answer her call and get into trouble for not being at school. His mind is made up for him as the voice rings out again.

'Our Jimmy, just you get over here, bad enough you playing hooky, never mind ignoring your Granny as well. Here now, do you hear me?'

I see them exchange the piece of paper and, with a final glance at me, the youth sets off, pleased to escape his Grandma.

I nod my thanks to the woman and, turning, I hasten back to the bedroom, falling over Mrs Plumb as I do.

12.40 p.m.

Mrs Grey smiles up at me, but her face is pale and she is lying back against the pillows. I go over and wipe her face with the flannel.

'Some problem with the afterbirth is there nurse? The other two took a fair time, but they came in the end. Is the baby all right?'

'Goodness yes, he's lovely,' I say.

I have to hold myself back so as not to rush over and check him, but I needn't worry, the delayed reaction voice speaks. 'Oh yes, he's lovely, just blinking his eyes at me he is, real cheeky, he is.'

I make no reply.

The knock comes, and I hurry to follow Mrs Plumb to the door. The large lady stands on the step, and I can see the tall thin youth behind her. The lady is puffing as she starts to speak, 'He says that . . .'

She draws in breath. The youth climbs the step, and speaks over her shoulder.

'There weren't no midwife there, but the woman said as how she would tell her when she did come in.'

He drops down a step and looks at me around the woman. She turns and wafts her hand across his head.

'Haven't got time to live nowadays, have they? And more cheek than sense most of 'em.'

I am not listening to the complaint, and, as the youth starts to turn away, I call to him.

'Do you know where the doctor's surgery is? I'll have a look who the doctor is.'

I start to turn to go and look for Mrs Grey's doctor's name, but the large lady intercedes, 'There's naught but one doctor around here, nurse, and he's at the surgery they built new up the top of the estate there.'

The youth is retreating rapidly down the path towards the gate.

'Could you run as fast as you can and fetch the doctor, tell him the same thing.'

He gets to the gate and turns, his lips puckered and his eyes narrowed he asks, 'What's in it for me?'

A loud voice beside me answers for me.

'A clip around the ear if you don't go, and you show some respect for the nurse when you talk to her.'

The large lady heads towards him, her hand raised. I call out, 'A shilling when you get back, if you hurry.'

Mrs Grey lies still, her face is now pallid, and her pulse feels thready. Her eyes open as I try to give a sip of water. Mrs Plumb has disappeared, she left stating that she had to get her husband's dinner ready. The baby has now gone to sleep, he is in need of his bath, but I check the forceps on his cord and all is well.

The bang comes on the door, and I am to it before the second bang sounds. The youth stands on the step, his face red.

'There ain't no doctor there, but they'll tell him when he comes back from his dinner, where's my shilling?'

His hand shoots out from the end of his loose sleeve, I fight my way into my pocket and almost in a dream I drop my last shilling into his hand. He turns and starts to examine his gains as he moves away, but I must stop him, I know that there is only one course of action left, I must send for the Flying Squad. Mrs Grey has lost too much blood, and she is still losing it, the emergency service from the Blood Transfusion Unit must be contacted. I call to his retreating back, my voice now small and cracked, 'Stop, young man.'

He comes to a halt, his black ringed eyes look at me over his shoulder, and his hand clamps shut over the shilling. I beckon him to come back, he steps one step towards me, but retains his running position ready should I demand the return of the money. I clear my throat and moisten my lips.

'I have a very important phone call for you to make, this one is life and death. Can you manage that, are you up to it?

He turns, and his chest puffs out as he steps back towards me and says, 'Yeah'.

I speak close to his ear.

'Ring nine, nine, nine. When someone answers, say that you want the Flying Squad. Tell them that the midwife sent you, and say the same as before, the afterbirth won't come. This is very important, you can't afford to get it wrong. You won't need any money, just ring the numbers.'

He repeats the instructions, and as I see his heels disappearing around the gate I shout, 'Do you know the address?'

He raises his hand as he runs.

1.15 p.m.

He stands by the gate directing the ambulance to the right address. Two men and a woman, all dressed in white, are in the room in a flash. Knocking me aside they surround the bed. A man dressed in green carries in a large box, and a drip stand rises at the side of the bed.

'What time was the delivery?' A voice asks.

I am about to reply, but the woman steps across to the notes which are lying on the dressing table, and calls out, 'Twelve fifteen.'

The man's voice asks, 'Have you got a blood group there by any chance?'

'AB positive,' the woman replies.

'Hum! Better put some O negative up, I don't trust some of these services.'

This man is starting to annoy me, and I am just about to step in to defend my profession when, through the corner of my eye, I see Mrs O'Reilly walking towards the gate. Quite a crowd has now gathered around the ambulance, and a young man carrying a black bag squeezes through them, and joins Mrs O'Reilly. Now I have everyone here, and I feel quite a fool, I should have managed this alone, I shouldn't have made all this fuss. Mrs O'Reilly turns from the group and steps over to me. She pushes me backwards towards the wall, her face is stern and her mouth is straight as she half whispers, 'So what happened here, then?'

Now I feel exhausted and overwhelmed but lifting my head high, I tell her the sequence of events.

'She was starting to bleed quite hard, I could do nothing else, I could leave her no longer.'

Her face softens and, turning she walks over and picks up the notes and reading them, she disappears back into the throng around the bed. I hear her voice saying, 'The call was absolutely essential.'

1.25 p.m.

A voice calls loud, 'Nurse, is there a nurse here?'

I hasten towards the voice, a hand is extended backwards, and it holds a large kidney dish in which lies the afterbirth. Without looking at me the voice says, 'Check that we have got all of it.'

I take the dish and retire to the bathroom. Returning a few minutes later, I call into the throng, 'Placenta and membranes are intact.'

No one thanks me, no one replies. I see Mrs O'Reilly talking to the man I had assumed to be the GP. I walk over and tell her that I am going to bath the baby. Mrs O'Reilly nods, and the baby and I disappear together into the bathroom.

1.40 p.m.

Mrs O'Reilly comes into the bathroom and looks down at the baby.

'Is he all right?' she asks.

'Yes he's fine,' I reply.

She nods, and then puts her hand on my shoulder.

'I've recorded the time of the delivery of the afterbirth.'

She stands behind me, her hand still on my shoulder as she speaks.

'You did well there, it took some courage to make that decision, but it was the right one, it is the one that I would have made.'

She squeezes my shoulder, and turns to go.

'They're giving her one pint of blood, and they're staying with her to see if she will need another. When you have finished with the baby we can go. I have told them that we will return this evening to check on Mrs Grey.'

She smiles down on me and leaves, the mood is sombre.

2.45 p.m.

I sit at the kitchen table, my head in my hands. The poached egg on toast lies before me untouched. Mrs O'Reilly comes into the kitchen as the kettle starts to whistle. I hear her voice as I look down on the eggs.

'Why are you so depressed? You did a good job, it is I who should be sorry, if I hadn't diverted off to the nunnery on the way home I would have been there when the call came.'

I pull a face, and don't look at her as I moan, 'Everything is going wrong for me, I don't seem to have one straightforward, normal case in my book.'

I hear her laugh as she replies, 'What is straightforward about having a baby? You ask any woman who's ever had one, every birth is packed with drama and the unexpected. The only thing you can do is to be prepared for all eventualities, and if mother and baby come out fit then you've done well. Whatever you had to do, and whatever it took, it was right.'

'The Flying Squad didn't think so,' I reply.

She pours boiling water into the teapot as she replies, 'I'm not here to worry about them, and neither are you.'

4.30 p.m.

The clinical room has been put in order and we are now sitting in the sitting room. I am trying to catch up with some midwifery reading for the exams and Mrs O'Reilly, as usual, is reading her paper. The phone rings, and before I can rise Mrs O'Reilly is on her feet and heading for the door.

'I'll get it. You get on with your studying.'

I hear her voice on the landing outside the door, she talks and listens for some time, so it can't be a delivery. I try to concentrate on my books. She comes back into the room, and sits in silence for some moment before she speaks.

'That was Dr Goode on the phone.'

She waits for my attention, I give it to her.

'He is Mrs Grey's GP, the one who came to her house at the delivery, you remember him?'

'Yes I remember him, what did he want?'

Now panic sounds in my voice as I continue, 'Has something happened to Mrs Grey?'

She laughs as she beckons me to sit.

'No! No! Nothing like that, it was a courtesy call. He has been to see Mrs Grey, the Flying Squad have gone, they gave her just one pint of blood, and she looks much better now. I told him that we would call in this evening, and that we would let him know how things were.'

She hesitates for a moment, still looking at my face, then she picks up her paper, and starts to look at it. Her voice comes from behind it.

'He said to thank you for your correct and rapid response to the emergency situation. He feels that there would have been no time to get her into hospital, and that your response was the correct and the only one available.'

She lowers the paper, and her smile is broad.

'How's that for praise?' she asks.

'And by the way, he says that you owe him a shilling. He paid the lad who did the running. He was still waiting by the gate when he visited Mrs Grey half an hour ago. He said he gave him the shilling, and a clip around the ear for not being in school. He said he told him he wanted to see him running in the school sports in the summer, told him that a lad who could run like that should go places, that is if he went to school regularly.'

I had forgotten the real hero of the day, in all my anxiety and self-concern, I had forgotten him. I feel angry with myself but smile realising he must have conned another shilling out of the doctor.

'Oh, I meant to go and thank him and I forgot he was the one who saved the day. Did Dr Goode thank him?'

She looks at me over her glasses.

'Well, he said that he is going up to the secondary school next week to organise some medicals. He said he would check up on him with the headmaster. That should put him in the eye of the needle, and buck up his chances, if he's got anything in him that is.'

I have to grin to myself when I think of the long skinny body and the large flappy ears standing in front of the headmaster and the doctor.

I hear her voice continue, 'By the way, I have secured a place for Mary Maloney with the nuns at St Cuthbert's. They have a small hostel, and the Mother Superior says Mary can stay there until the baby is ready for discharge and Mary has found some place to take her.'

20

Wednesday 25th April

8.30 a.m.

I have a full day ahead of me. My wheels spin, and warm air whizzes past me as I speed down the hill towards town. The road looks brighter and the trees, which overhang the road, are starting to look greener. I want to get to the hospital before Mary is discharged; I want to make sure that she is going to the hostel and not back to her old address. I swing off my bike and wheel it into the porter's lodge. The boy in the lodge, who doesn't look much older than my runner of yesterday, claims it. He speaks in his most manly voice, which cracks a little on the last note, 'I'll see to that for you, nurse.'

I thank him and almost run along the corridor to get to Mary's bedside, but I need not have worried, for the back of a grey habit almost shields Mary from my view. I stop behind the nun who stands at the bottom of the bed, a little uncertain what to do; I know I have a role to play in the present events but at this moment I'm not sure what it is, so I speak to the nun, 'Oh, good morning, Sister.'

She turns and looks down at me; nuns always seem to be tall. I can see Mary's face behind her – if it were to become any redder it would light up the ward.

'Oh good morning to you, nurse,' the distinctly Irish voice replies.

I look around her grey habit at the gleaming face.

'Good morning, Mary, are you off to your new home?' I ask.

She does not speak, but looks at me with imploring eyes.

The nun passes over a dress, which she has obviously brought with her, and helps Mary into it as she speaks, 'Indeed she is, and who, may I ask, are you?'

Now she turns the full glare of the bright blue eyes on me, and I find myself either wanting to fall on one knee or curtsy. I hold fast against the urge, I have to stand up for Mary, we have got her this far, so instead I reply, 'I am the midwife who delivered her, and I will be looking after her for the next week.'

The face splits and white teeth show in a beaming smile.

'Oh to be sure, the Mother Superior said that we would be seeing you.'

She extends a hand from inside the habit and, taking mine, she shakes it vigorously.

'Miss Naomi Ann will be staying in the hospital for a while, but the Church is not too far away, and Mary will be able to spend time with her daughter.'

She lowers her voice, and smiles at Mary, 'And, we hope, breastfeed her.'

Mary smiles back at the nun and the roses on her cheeks lose some of their fire. I am relieved and my shoulders sink down. Things look okay, and at least Naomi Ann has managed to keep her name.

10.30 a.m.

I turn into Mrs Grey's pathway. It has been a long ride from the hospital and I feel that my legs will fall off. The climb and the sun shining have done me no good at all. I am pleased when Mr Grey opens the door. Mrs Plumb is in the bedroom, but I am glad that I don't have to deal with her today – yesterday was more than enough for me. Mrs Grey is now fine, and Mr Grey says that she now has more roses in her cheeks than he has seen for years. I assure him that there are much better ways of achieving the same effect. He nods as he takes her hand.

'Yes, nurse, I think that we will have to try and get away for a bit of a break this summer.'

She smiles up at him and, as I take her pulse, I murmur to the two of them, 'And now that you've got your son maybe a bit of a break on that front too, hey?'

His eyes meet mine, and his face reddens.

'A cup of tea is it, nurse? I know these two can always drink one.'

He returns with the tea and, as he hands me one of the best china cups, he speaks. 'That young doctor has already been chewing my ear, you two been talking together?'

I smile, drink my tea, write up the notes and leave. As he escorts me to the door I ask, 'Who was that young lad who took all my messages yesterday?'

The smile covers his face, and I realise that he is much younger than I had at first thought him to be.

'Oh, that was Jimmy McDonald, I understand that I owe him.'

'Yes, he was a good lad, he did everything I asked of him without question.'

He looks across at me.

'Doctor said it cost him a shilling. But I'll see what I can do.

He stands by the bike as I load the bag.

'Where does he live?' I ask. I intend to pay him a visit.

He nods his head sideways towards the gap in the fence, which I know leads through to that part of the council estate in which the Waller family live.

'He lives with his gran at the other side of the estate,

never goes to school; she doesn't care much about him, well he doesn't look as though she does.'

He muses for a moment and then, steadying my bike for me, he speaks almost to himself, 'I run a bit of a football club, just for the kids like, I'll see his gran and him, maybe he'll like to join.'

He looks at me as I stand by the bike, and smiles at me. 'We need a good winger, if he can run that fast he'll do. And thank you, nurse, I understand I owe my wife's life to you.'

Now it is my turn to blush, and as I cycle off he shouts, 'You don't want to come and play goalie, do you?'

I raise my hand in thanks and shout back, 'No thanks, just give young Jimmy a game.'

12.30 p.m.

I am sitting by the kitchen table. Mrs O'Reilly is sitting with me and we are writing Mrs Grey's delivery into my Case Book. I am doing the writing and Mrs O'Reilly is checking to make sure that every detail is recorded accurately. She has not helped me with any of my other cases, but then this is the first time that the Flying Squad have been called out. This afternoon I must present my Case Book. I had hoped to have twelve cases in it and some of them normal deliveries, but it is not to be.

2.30 p.m.

The classroom is noisy. Everyone has arrived and everyone carries their Case Book. Several people are proclaiming that they have completed all twelve cases, and can now hand in their Case Books in preparation for the examination. Maureen is one of these, and I can hear her voice as she talks loudly to some of the other students. She has not spoken to me since the party, and although I have several questions that I would like to ask her, I really don't want to start up the conversation. I have not heard from Tony since the party either and I don't intend to go into the Student Union building today.

Miss Bland, the Senior Tutor, enters the room, and silence falls. She addresses us in a clear crisp voice that matches her whole appearance as her eyes scan across us.

'Good afternoon, nurses.'

She smiles and waits for us to reply. Some of us had stood when she arrived, and now seating ourselves we reply, 'Good afternoon, Miss Bland.'

She looks down at a sheet of paper which she carries in her right hand and threads the chain to her glasses through her left hand. Raising her eyes she looks at us and addresses us again.

'Nurses, I hope I'll be able to call you midwives in a few weeks.'

She gives a tight little laugh, and we all respond in like manner.

'As I am sure you are all aware, the viva exams will be taking place in three weeks time.'

A murmur travels across the assembled hopefuls. She raises the hand which holds the glasses, and the silver chain sparkles.

'I wish to remind you that all Case Books must be in on Tuesday May 6th. It is hoped that all students will by then have twelve completed cases written up. Should this not be possible the cases should be written to their state of completion on April 29th, and the Case Book should be presented to the student's tutor on that date. A decision as to whether the student is eligible to enter the exam will be made, and the student will be notified.'

A murmur rises again, and out of the corner of my eye I see the student sitting at the desk next to me pat her book.

The tutor coughs to reclaim our attention and continues, 'Would you please line up in alphabetical order, and Miss Perkins will tell you which tutor to visit.'

She smiles a smile as stiff and crisp as she is, turns, and is gone.

I know that Maureen will be standing behind me in the line up, as it is in alphabetical order, and this has been one of the things that as always thrown us together. She stands behind me studiously ignoring me as she talks with the girl behind her. Then I hear her voice directed at me. She doesn't address me directly she just speaks, but I know that she is talking to me.

'I hear Tony is going to play in that tournament, representing the hospital, quite a thing so they say. I hear he asked the Prof's daughter to play with him, I think that she said yes. Getting quite thick, are those two.'

I look straight ahead, my face burns, and I have no intention of facing her. I can see the pretty, white, pleated skirt, and the foot lifting gracefully behind it as she serves, and I think that the relationship will not be a long one if it is a knock-out tournament.

I face Miss Perkins and, without her having to ask, I say, 'Eight completed, three partial.'

She glances up and nods her head over towards her door, I join those already waiting. As I leave I hear Maureen's voice, 'Twelve completed, and I have delivered one extra.'

I don't wait to hear more.

4.30 p.m.

Mrs O'Reilly isn't in. I knock on her door but no one answers. I run down the stairs, Mrs Stone is ironing in the kitchen.

'Has Mrs O'Reilly gone out?'

I try to keep my voice light but I know that panic edges it, I do hope that she has not been called out to a delivery while I have been away. Just glancing up from the shirt she is wrestling with, Mrs Stone nods her head.

'Haven't seen her for an hour or so, said she was going down to the Nunnery by the Catholic Church.'

She laughs, and looks across at me.

'Maybe she's gone to sign you up.'

I give her a weak smile, and head back up the stairs. Almost before I arrive at the kitchen I hear the front door bang, and Mrs O'Reilly's footsteps sound on the stairs. I have made tea and, as she sinks into her usual chair the evening paper before her, I pour two cups.

'I've just been down to see the nuns, wanted to check if young Mary had settled in.'

She takes a sip of tea and I search through the biscuit tin.

'Seems she's the model client, and young Naomi is doing well, the Sisters reckon that it won't be long before she will be heading home to Ireland.'

I almost choke on the biscuit. I had assured my tutor that Mary Maloney would remain until her tenth day had been completed, and that I had access to the baby. I had planned to visit Mary tomorrow and every day for the next week, but were Mrs O'Reilly and the nuns going to take over her care? I am coughing and can't get my words out, Mrs O'Reilly gets there first.

'She won't be going before next week, will she? It's only her second day today.'

She looks at my startled face and laughs, 'You in trouble with those tutors again?'

I don't reply. She does not seem to be taking the issue seriously.

21

Thursday 26th April

8.30 a.m.

I am heading down the hill towards the main road with all
the speed that I can muster. I know that St Cuthbert's
Church lies just behind the large houses that edge the
main road leading into the city. Mrs O'Reilly had told
me that the convent lies just behind the church on a road
named Convent Road, how original I had thought, but
now I am pleased that the road is named after the building
I seek, I don't have to remember another name.

Saint Cuthbert's stands dark, red and powerful, its
façade impenetrable with a sealed oak door. Heavy wire
frames cover its hidden lead windows. I ride along Church
Road, which fronts the church; it is still and silent. A dog
trots towards me and lifts its leg against some weeds that
grow from the bottom of one of the church's rising red
pillars, it sniffs the pillar, attempts another marking and,
being unsuccessful, moves on. Off to my right the gloomy
exterior of the church extends on, every facet solid and
inaccessible. A woman appears, she walks towards the back
of the church, so, throwing my leg over the bike, I press
my foot down on the pedal, and head towards her. The
path lies beneath the branches of the yew tree, and small
brown shells cover the narrow lane as the yew tree
struggles to open its first fruits of the year. The small
square of grass beneath its boughs fights to show an

occasional blade of green, and these do battle with the nettles which threaten to overpower all that lies beneath the tree. Rusty iron railings support some of the tree branches, and the lane is barred by an equally rusty gate which crosses the lane and joins the railings to the church. As I stand one foot on either side of my bike, I see movement beyond the gate and the head and shoulders of the woman appear. Stepping from my bike I wheel it towards the gate, the woman stands with her back to me, and I can hear water running. Then I realise that I am standing at an entrance to the church graveyard. A cobbled path runs off to my left and old moss-covered gravestones lean unkempt among the grass and weeds. The woman rises and, holding a watering can before her, she turns. She seems not to see me as I stand behind the gate, so I clear my throat before I speak.

'Excuse me, I wonder if you could tell me . . .'

I get no further with my request as she turns and, with fire in her voice, she calls out, 'Who's there? What do you want?'

She is a portly woman in her middle years. Her dress is plain and comfortable, and I assume her persona is usually calm, but now she holds the watering can towards me as if it were a weapon of defence. I mumble as I move the bike back from the gate.

'Oh, I'm sorry if I startled you, I just wanted directions to Convent Road.'

Now she is by the gate and looking at me and, as she puts the watering can by her feet, she smiles up at me.

'Sorry nurse, it's just that we have had a lot of vandals in the churchyard, and as you can see we have few people to help us to maintain the graves.'

She turns and waves her arm energetically towards the old stones, which, without word, convey their feelings of neglect.

'But you are not a vandal, and am I to assume that you are Nurse Compton?'

Mary Maloney stands with her back towards me as I enter the room. She is leaning over a narrow bed, one of four in the white, wooden floored, small square room, and at the moment she is the only person in the room apart from the Virgin Mary, who stands, child in arms, her almost life-size body pressed against the far wall. The nun holds the door open for me and I squeeze past, my bag held before me.

The woman, whose name, I discovered, is Fran, and I had walked through the graveyard, me wheeling my bike and Fran carrying her watering can.

'Oh no, I'm not one of the nuns, nurse, God bless us, I just come in to help now and then. I help look after the girls who come in. We have three at the moment, Mary is the only one with us, the other two are in hospital having their babies.'

She had crossed herself a couple of times during this conversation, and did it again as she opened a large brown door in an otherwise doorless and windowless red brick wall, which seems to run almost the length of Convent Road. We had not walked far since we left the cemetery, but I was quite lost, and even the large church seemed to have disappeared behind trees. We entered a dark, wood-clad corridor, lit only by an occasional wall lamp. A nun, dressed in black cowl and a black dress covered by a grey apron, passed us on the corridor. She did not speak but the movement of her head conveyed a greeting. In silence we moved down the corridor, I was pleased that my shoes were rubber-soled, anything else would have made too much noise. Light flooded the corridor as a figure, similarly dressed to the one who had just passed us, minus the apron, had stepped into our view. My guide stopped and, after crossing herself, had said, 'Mother, this is Nurse Compton. She has come to see Mary.'

The grey eyes look at me, and I feel as I do when Mrs O'Reilly disapproves of me. The voice is light, with a slight Irish accent.

'We hope that Mary and the baby will both do well.'

The eyes leave my face and I know from experience that I have been dismissed.

Mary turns towards me as I cross the room. Her face is red and her eyes are swollen as she pulls the sleeve of the long white nightdress across her face. Gone is the paint and the powder, gone is the brash chatty girl, and at that moment I thought, gone is hope.

'Hello, Mrs Maloney, how are you?'

I hear the door click closed behind me, we are alone. She moves towards me with some speed, and I almost have to catch her as she lands in my arms.

'Oh, Nurse Compton, I am so pleased to see you; I don't know how I am going to survive here.'

Tears are running down her face and are wetting my dress. Pulling her back towards the bed, I coax her to sit. I had thought that she might be feeling rather down, it is common for even the most experienced and stable woman to feel depressed about three days after the birth, but now, as I look around this austere room with its white walls and smell of polish, I can understand Mary's feelings.

'Is there only you here?' I ask.

Snuffling into her nightdress sleeve again she looks up at me.

'I've heard some other voices, but I think that I have to stay here because I haven't got a baby to feed.'

As she speaks she plays with something behind her on the bed and I realise that it is a bundle of baby clothes.

'Have you got some clothes for Naomi? Do let me see them.'

Her face brightens as we look at the small clothes which the nuns have provided, and we laugh as we see how large they will be for Naomi.

I have examined Mary and all is well and as I head for the door, the lady who had seen me in arrives.

'Is all well?' she asks.

Before I can answer she continues, 'I hope it is because Sister Magdalene is driving down to the General Hospital in half an hour, and if Mary can be dressed in time she'll take her down to visit Naomi.'

10.00 a.m.

Tomorrow I must ask if Mary can move in with the other girls who are there. I'm sure that she will feel better with company, after all it is not that she will become depressed with girls who have babies, she does have a baby of her own. I did not see anyone on my way out, but now, as I ride along beside the cemetery, my mind returns to my main problem, the twelfth delivery.

10.30 a.m.

The phone rings, I leap to my feet and, almost knocking a chair over, I rush to pick up the instrument.

'Mrs O'Reilly's residence, Pupil Midwife Compton speaking, how might I help you?'

'Good morning, Pupil Midwife Compton, is Midwife O'Reilly in?'

I know the voice, it is Mrs O'Reilly's friend. My voice sinks as I reply, No, she's gone to a meeting at the Council House in town, can I give her a message when she comes back?'

'No thanks, I'll ring later.'

The phone goes dead. I stand with the mouthpiece in my hand, and look down at it.

'Why don't you ring with one of the cases?' I ask the offending object. It does not reply.

I hang up the mouthpiece, and return to the kitchen and my books. There are four women who are either overdue, or just due. This morning I have already visited the two who are overdue. I was at one house at eight this morning; I nearly frightened the poor woman to death, she thought that something was wrong. But no, not a contraction in sight, just the poor woman puffing around trying to get two children to school. I have just returned from the second visit. Here the lady's husband had stayed away from work because his wife had said that she did not feel well. I had listened to the baby's heart, and had felt her abdomen in the hope that she was in early labour. But after half an hour of walking around the small garden and a hot cup of tea, she had given an enormous belch, and said that she felt much better. She is a very large lady, and she should have given birth ten days ago according to her dates but now she has returned to sitting by the table, and her husband has gone back to work.

12.00 *midday*

I hear the front door open and close, I know that Mrs O'Reilly will take some little time to come up to the flat as she will stop and have a chat with Mrs Stone. I wait anxiously for her steps to sound on the stairs, I know that I am being ridiculous but I am hopeful that she will have collected a woman's case notes from the Department and that the delivery will be imminent. I know from her past visits that although work is sent through the post, there are times when the midwives are due to visit the Department the post is not sent, but is instead collected during the visit. She has removed her coat, and now takes off her hat and hangs it behind the door.

'Goodness, it's getting warm out there, warm for this time of year anyway. I've got a case for you; I've left it downstairs in the clinical room.'

My heart leaps in hope; I'll get my twelfth delivery in time. I fall down the stairs two at a time and I am in the clinical room with the notes in my hands within seconds. I look at them for some time before the truth hits me. The notes are almost complete, the baby has been delivered, it was delivered in hospital. I look at the section referring to the baby. It tells me that a female infant was born, that it was at term, it also tells me that it was dead at birth. I turn the notes over as if seeking for more information.

Mrs O'Reilly's step sounds as she enters the room, she doesn't speak for a moment, and then her voice is low, 'Seems we've got the fluffy lollipop, I saw her quite early in her pregnancy, but not after she was about four months. She had a bad time all the way through and her GP sent her in to hospital. I suppose he will be going to see her. Sorry I haven't got any more information on what exactly happened, but I thought that it would be advisable for one of us to go along to see her this morning to check how she is. Nip along before we eat, I've got some paperwork to do so I'll wait dinner for you.'

She smiles at me and is gone.

12.10 p.m.

I cycle down towards the park. I know the road in which she lives; it runs along the opposite side of the park, that is, opposite to the council estate. I have taken a moment to look at the notes, and I know that she is thirty eight years of age, and that she has two children who are both at secondary school. Mrs O'Reilly had said to see how she was; I had a good idea how she was. I should have had a sister who would now have been ten years old, but she did not live. I had looked after my mother and I knew how she felt.

I arrive at the house and, opening the gate, I wheel my bike up the path and knock on the door. A woman of about my own height opens the door. For a moment she hesitates, and then, recognising the uniform, she steps back and invites me in.

'Oh hello, nurse, kind of you to come to see me, I wasn't really expecting you.'

She turns and walks across a small hall and through a doorway. I mumble something about being pleased to come to see her and, closing the front door, I follow her into what is a light and pleasant sitting-room. This is a well-presented room, and for a moment my eyes wander around it as I admire its furnishings and ornaments. I raise my eyes to speak to her but she is not there. For a moment I can't see her, and then I see her move as she pushes herself from the wall by a door which lies under the alcove made by the stairs. She blows air out through pursed lips as she moves away from the wall and back towards the centre of the room.

'Are you all right?' I ask.

I step towards her; the obvious shortage of breath has taken me by surprise. She stands and stretches, her head and shoulders upright as she breaths through pursed lips, her face pale.

'Do sit down, Mrs Wood, you look quite exhausted.'

I move towards her, my hand raised inviting her to sit. 'Don't you think that you would be better in bed?'

I look at her face, it is pale but not only pale. Now that I stand closer I can see that her lips look rather blue, and that her nose looks tight and white with a blue tinge around it. I put my arm around her shoulders as I try to guide her towards the settee and coax her to sit.

'Do sit down, Mrs Wood, I would like to take your pulse, and have a talk with you.'

She sinks to the settee and, with a deep sigh, looks at me.

'I don't know, all this fuss, I can't seem to get anything right any more can I? Just one thing after another.'

She puts her hands over her face and starts to cry. Putting my arm around her I pull her to me and fight hard to hold back my tears as I hold her. She takes a handkerchief from her apron pocket and mops her face.

'Can't spend the rest of my life dwelling on it can I? Our Ruth has taken it badly, particularly when she found out it was a girl, she always wanted a sister, but look at me sitting here and you haven't had a cup of tea, where are my manners?'

Her face looks a little brighter now, and I wonder if her poor colour had been due to stress.

She returns with a tray held before her. On it rest cups and saucers, but before she has passed through the kitchen door she stretches upwards again and shouts out. I grab the tray, milk runs down my dress and sugar sprays across the flowered carpet as I step over the china cup in an attempt to stop her falling. She leans against the wall as I pull over a high-backed chair, and lower her into it. Her pulse is rapid and irregular and her breathing is shallow. Her face is now completely devoid of colour except for the blue around the nose and lips, and she sits with her shoulders raised and head held high. I whisper close to her face as I hold her wrist, 'Mrs Wood, can you tell me where the pain is?'

She swallows, and her shoulders drop a little as she speaks almost through a sigh, 'It sort of aches all the time around here when I breathe.'

She rubs her hands around her chest, and then looks at me with a worried and startled face.

'But that was a big one nurse, when I lifted the tray . . .'

She doesn't finish the sentence, but again stands and then walks towards the window.

'The doctor should be here, George said that he would ring the surgery when he got to work, these pains have kept us both awake.'

Frantically my mind races through all the sheaths of notes that I have ever written, and all the lectures that I have endured. There is something familiar to me here, and then I remember an elderly lady who had been admitted for a hernia operation on my last surgical ward. She had very bad varicose veins and the anaesthetist had been concerned. He had asked us to watch out for any chest pains when she came back from theatre and, sure enough, on her third day, post-operative pains, such as Mrs Wood is now having, were noted. She was diagnosed as having a pulmonary embolism.

'Mrs Wood, did you have any varicose veins while you were carrying?'

She looks at me with exhausted eyes, 'Yes, nurse, I've had them for years but they got bad when I was carrying, I had to wear special stockings.'

12.25 p.m.

The phone box is on the corner. I have done a walk-cum-run down to it, but now a man stands inside. He leans on the wall, and talks as he watches me approach, now he turns his back on me, and starts to fish in his pocket for more money. I run around the box, and drag the door open.

'Excuse me, may I use the phone?'

Pushing in beside him, I thrust my nurse's badge up

towards his face as I almost shout, 'This is a medical emergency.'

He looks down at me and then, turning back to the phone, says, 'Sorry love, I'll have to ring you again, some nutter here says she has a medical emergency. Yes, yes, love you lots, ring you later.'

I am in the box with him now and I take the phone from him before he has time to put it down. Pressing the hand rest down I hear the ring tone, and dialling 999 I wait for the voice.

'Police, ambulance or fire, which service do you require?'

'Ambulance.'

The man still stands in the box with me, his mouth now hangs open. A voice at the other end of the line speaks, 'Ambulance service here, how may I help you?'

My throat feels dry, and I give a little cough, the man looks down at me expectantly.

'This is a midwife speaking, I require an ambulance for a woman who has a post-partum pulmonary embolism, could you please hurry as she has been in pain for some time?'

'What's your address, nurse?'

I can't remember the address. Turning to the man, who is now standing with one foot on the pavement, I almost shout, 'What's the name of this road?'

He looks down at me for a moment and then, taking his cue from me, shouts as he leans towards the phone, 'It's Hawthorn Drive, it's just off Park Lane.'

'Thank you, sir, I've got you, will you please stay with your wife, we will be with you in minutes, sir.'

The phone goes dead, I smile at the man.

'He thinks that you are the husband.'

'Of whom?'

He asks the question as I squeeze past him. And I call to

him as I set off back to Mrs Wood, 'Of the woman who's had the baby.'

I hear his anguished cry.

'Oh my God, don't tell the girlfriend, she'll never believe me.'

He is still agonising to himself as I turn into Mrs Wood's gate.

12.35 p.m.

The ambulance arrives. I have managed to get Mrs Wood to sit down on the high-backed chair; I have tried to explain what is happening but her anxiety levels are so high I'm sure that she understands little. At the sound of the ambulance bell her next-door neighbour arrives, and we have just enough time to make the arrangements for Mr Wood to be notified. The ambulance leaves with bells ringing. I step back into the house to wait for Mr Wood to arrive, but as I pull the door to it doesn't close. A tall man in a dark grey suit stands in the doorway.

'Excuse me, is Mrs Wood in?'

I look towards him, my goodness he got here quickly I think.

'Oh, Mr Wood . . .'

I get no further as the young man interrupts me.

'I am not Mr Wood, I am Dr Wainwright, I am Mrs Wood's GP.'

Explanations and apologies are given.

'What made you think that it was a pulmonary embolism?' he asks.

I tell him about the case that I had nursed.

'I'll follow the ambulance in, and check up on her.'

With that, he is gone. I wait until Mr Wood arrives, and then leave.

Mrs O'Reilly is sitting at the kitchen table, which is almost covered with pieces of paper. She looks up as I walk in, looks at her watch and mumbles, 'Where have you been?'

I sink down on the chair beside the table.

'Can nothing I do go right, or, should I say, can nothing be straightforward?'

I start to tell her what has happened when the phone rings. She disappears and I put on the kettle. Dinner is late today. I can hear her talking on the landing, her voice sounds very professional in tone, not her usual voice for talking to friends. She walks into the kitchen, and stands in the doorway.

'That was a Dr Wainwright on the phone.'

A cold chill goes up my spine; there was nothing wrong with Mrs Wood, and I have wasted everyone's time.

'Mrs Wood did have a pulmonary embolism, and you will be pleased to know that they got her to the hospital and on to treatment just in time. There is every hope that she will recover. Dr Wainwright wishes to thank you for making such an accurate diagnosis, and for responding so rapidly. Now can you tell me what happened this time?'

22

Thursday 26th April

9.30 a.m.

The Case Book lies open on the kitchen table; I have read through all the completed cases, and now know I them off by heart. Mrs Waller is completed, and so is Mrs Copperopolis, and I have encountered no major problems. But as I turn the page a major, major problem faces me: the section for recording case number twelve lies pristine clean and virgin white. I sigh and rub my fingers across the space.

'Come on one of you, ring, one of you must go into labour today.'

I have already ridden down to see Mrs Grey. Mr Grey was still at home, but he will be returning to work tomorrow. Mrs Plumb has said that she will hold the fort; I think that I might have to round up a tribe of Apaches to come down with me if I am to get through her defences, or maybe I'll call on young McDonald again. Mr Grey has been to see him and his gran, and I was very pleased to hear he is going to join the football club; Mr Grey already has an old pair of boots ready for him so he has no excuse.

But no more waffling around, what am I going to do about that empty space in the Case Book? According to the notes two women are overdue, one by as much as ten days. I had been to see her yesterday afternoon but she was marching around her house, her large form taking up most of its space, with not a sign of a contraction to be seen. I think that Mrs March will give birth to a baby elephant in a couple of months' time.

9.40 a.m.

I decide to pay Mrs March another visit, and if nothing is happening I will have a word with Mrs O'Reilly about getting things moving.

I am carrying my examination bag down the stairs when the front door bursts open and Mrs O'Reilly comes through it talking to someone behind her.

'Come in, I'll put the kettle on, I want to hear all about this.'

Seeing me, she stops and, turning to the tall young woman who has just entered the hallway, she speaks to her as she waves her hand towards me.

'Oh, I'm glad that she's not gone out yet. Miss Brown, this is Nurse Compton, she is my present Pupil Midwife, I know that she will be interested in it. Nurse Compton, this is Miss Brown, one of my colleagues, and one of my ex-pupils.'

Mrs O'Reilly laughs as she pushes past me, and I smile at the young woman whose fuzz of red hair now passes my face. I hear them talking as they enter the kitchen. I'm not sure if I have been invited to join them, so I remain on the stairs. I hear Mrs O'Reilly call as the cups rattle.

'Nurse Compton, come up here, and listen to this.'

Dropping my bag in the clinical room I head for the kitchen. I slide into the room. Mrs O'Reilly is pouring tea and the redhead is pulling papers from her handbag. Putting a teacup on the corner of the table, Mrs O'Reilly nods for me to sit. She speaks to me while looking at Miss Brown.

'Miss Brown has just been to Paris with her fiancé. As

part of this romantic episode she and her fiancé went to a Lamaze Clinic.'

I smile and nod my congratulations, for what I'm not sure, maybe for having a fiancé, or for going to Paris, or even for going to a Lamaze Clinic, although I'm not sure what that is.

'Yes, it was very interesting.'

She smiles a beautiful white smile, and the brown eyes look at me; again I'm not sure what bit we are talking about as being interesting. Now Mrs O'Reilly pulls out a chair and sits beside her. The papers from the handbag lie in front of her, and she turns them over and looks at the back of them as she speaks, 'So do they manage to have childbirth without pain? Did you actually attend a delivery? Is it just the delivery that is painless? Or is the whole labour painless?'

She turns the papers over again, and then calls out to me, 'Nurse Compton, can you read French by any chance?'

Jumping to attention and nearly knocking over my tea, I mumble my reply, 'No, I'm afraid I can read very little French, just school stuff, you know.'

'Um, so we won't get much from this then, will we?'

Mrs O'Reilly takes one final look at the written word, and then puts the papers back down on the table. Putting her cup down, and smiling at us Miss Brown pulls the papers towards her.

'To answer your questions, yes we saw a woman in labour, and we saw a delivery, we also went to an antenatal class. They have breathing exercises, and yes, the woman seemed not to be in much pain during her labour.'

My interest has now been raised, and I ask, 'What about the delivery, how did they manage that?'

The brown eyes look at me and twinkle, and in a

pompous voice she says, 'They just shout *poussez, poussez* at the woman.'

Now she bursts out laughing as she speaks.

'*Poussez* means push, Nurse Compton.'

She directs her face towards me, and in a mocking voice repeats the word, '*Poussez! Poussez!*'

I don't like this woman, I think that it is time to leave. Nodding my thanks for the translation I rise, and with a stiff smile say, 'Talking about pushing, I think that I had better go and see if my good woman is ready to *poussez, poussez*, very nice to have met you Miss Brown. Goodbye.'

10.00 a.m.

A fresh breeze blows in my face, it takes away some of my anger as I set off down the hill and out to the council estate. The March family live on the outskirts of the estate on Factory Lane. This so-called lane runs down the city side of the park, and eventually, after a couple of twists and turns, connects the estate to the main road which runs into the city. The houses at its upper end are not council houses but are rows of cottages which had, many years ago, been built to house workers for the small factories, some of which have survived the bombs, and still skirt Factory Lane on its way into town. The row of houses in which the March family live are kept in quite a prim state, and their occupants are always proud to proclaim their separate tenure and their distance from the council estate. Although the houses open directly onto the pavement at the front, all seem to have good-sized back gardens, and the back garden is Mr March's pride and joy.

I drop off my bike at the end of the row and wheel it down the side of the end house. The dirt track which runs along the back of the houses is edged by high fences, but I know which gate leads into number 26. I enter by the garden gate because Mrs March had told me that when the weather is warm she spends most of her time in the garden. It is warm today and she had been in the garden at my last visit. Before I have closed the gate behind me her large corpulent frame appears by the back door and beckons me to hurry. Her face is red, and she breathes heavily as she calls out.

'Oh, did she get you that quick? She must have hurried, I only just got back to the house.'

Leaning my bike against a small fence, I gather up my bag, and head towards her with hope in my heart.

'What has happened, Mrs March? Have the contractions started?'

I try to keep the note of hope out of my voice, but in one moment she quells my hope. 'Oh no, nurse, I haven't had any pains yet, but come on in and let me tell you.'

She turns and heads back through the kitchen door, I wince at the word 'pains' when referring to contractions, but wince even more at the pain of my own dashed hopes. I follow her into the kitchen, and she closes the door behind us.

'No, I've not had no pains, nurse, but my waters have broken.'

She demonstrates what had happened with a downward swish of her hands. She repeats it twice with some force, and although I know how much water will have come, I am compelled to glance at the floor to make sure that the water is not lapping over my shoe tops. My hopes rise, labour has started, so putting down my bag on a dry bit of floor, I try to calm her.

'Just tell me what happened, Mrs March, tell me nice and slowly.'

She sighs, and leans against the sink.

'I was just standing here doing the breakfast pots.'

She demonstrates the position in relationship to the sink.

'When whoosh down it came.'

Once again she demonstrates the force of the fall. Undoing my coat, now that the door is closed the door seems very warm, I ask, 'Just how much water was there, Mrs March? Did it run down your leg and wet your shoe, or did it run onto the floor?'

'Oh, it didn't wet the floor.'

She rubs her foot in front of her as if to proclaim that her floor is always pristine clean.

I pick up my bag, and smile at her. 'I think that you are in labour, Mrs March, I think that we had better go upstairs so that I can examine you to see what is happening.'

Her face goes even redder, and she puts her hands up to her hot cheeks.

'Oh, but my mother has gone away today, she has taken the little boy over to see his aunty.'

With a sigh she turns and, puffing as she pulls her large frame up each step, she climbs the stairs ahead of me. As she reaches the top she complains over her shoulder, 'I haven't felt no pains yet, nurse.'

10.30 a.m.

I have examined her and I am pleased to say that labour has most certainly started. I have felt the baby's head, it is firmly engaged. Only the forewaters have burst, the baby is fine. I almost whistle to myself as I place the yet empty notes on the dressing table and enter the first findings. I turn and, smiling, give her the results. 'You are in early labour, Mrs March.'

She starts to get off the bed but I halt her.

'I think that you had better spend some time in bed as

the waters have gone. You can get up to the toilet but I don't think that you should be climbing up and down stairs.'

She looks at me with wide eyes as she sinks back onto the bed.

'But my mother is away, how can I stop in bed?'

'I can ask your next-door neighbour to pop in and see you, or we can send for your husband to come home, but I don't think much will happen before dinner time.'

She sighs and looks across at me as she nods her head to her right pointing to the house next door.

'You can ask *her* if she will come in.'

She then holds her hand out to her left.

'But don't go to *her* or my mother will have a fit.'

She closes her eyes and puts her head back against the pillows.

10.45 a.m.

All has been arranged and I have left a gleeful neighbour, who is, at this moment, just nipping in with a cup of tea.

11.45 a.m.

I have been to see Mary, and I was very relieved to note that without my having to ask, the nuns had moved her into a room with two other girls, and today she looks much brighter. Naomi gained weight yesterday, and the hospital is hoping that she will be able to be discharged in one week. Mary will have to stay with the nuns as Naomi will have to return to the clinic at the hospital for some time, even after she is discharged. Mary seemed to be quite happy about this, and she was smiling brightly when she gave me her news.

'The nuns have contacted mama, and my uncle will be

coming over to collect us both as soon as the Mother Superior says that we can go.'

Mary was also keen to tell me that the priest had been to the hospital, and the baby had been christened. She was now legally named Naomi Ann Dorothy.

'Lovely name isn't it and not a Mary in sight; the priest said that it can't be changed now, because I have also been and had her registered, so it is on the church register, on the register at the council, and on her birth certificate.'

Mary's smile stretches from ear to ear as she waves the piece of paper at me.

On my way back from the hospital I have called into Mrs O'Reilly's house to collect a delivery bag and a gas and air machine. I am pleased to note that Miss Brown has left. Mrs O'Reilly is also not in – another one of the ladies, who is overdue, has rung and Mrs O'Reilly has gone to investigate. I leave all the messages with Mrs Stone, and hasten back to Mrs March. Hoping against hope that Mrs March delivers normally and quickly, and that the delivery which Mrs O'Reilly is attending doesn't outshine mine, I carry the delivery bag and the gas and air machine up the narrow staircase.

12.10 p.m.

For the third time I ask Mrs March if she is having any contractions. Her reply remains the same, 'No nurse, I can't really say that I am, one or two sort of twinges and cramps, but no, not proper pains.'

She has again picked up the knitting, and again she has turned her eyes to the pattern. I am beginning to tire of the baby's smiling face which smirks at me from the front page of the knitting pattern. A piping voice calls up the stairs, 'Does anyone up there want a cup of tea?'

Without taking her eyes from the knitting, Mrs March calls out, 'Yes please, Mrs White, I'd love a cup.'

I just mumble, 'Yes please,' as I examine the notes for the twentieth time. There is no doubt the membranes have ruptured. On external examination the head feels well engaged, and as far as I could tell at the last internal examination, labour had started and everything was moving along. I sigh as the tea is pressed into my hand and a thought crosses my mind, maybe Mrs March has been over to France, and has taken some classes for painless childbirth – she is certainly managing without a single *poussez, poussez* in sight. In a muse I wonder how I will know when the baby is due to be born if Mrs March feels no urge to push, but what I do know is that if labour has stopped at this point, then Mrs March will have to be sent into hospital, and my twelfth delivery will be gone.

Out of the corner of my eye I see Mrs White walking across the room and I see the knitting appear on the side of the bed. I see Mrs March raise her buttocks as if to push herself up the bed and then I hear the cry. Mrs March is lying back against the pillows, she has her mouth wide open, and she is shouting out in full voice. Mrs White jumps backwards as if she has been shot, and the teacup pours its contents on the bedside rug. I also jump but in three strides I am at Mrs March's side. She is hanging onto the back of the bed and is almost pulling the wooden frame from is anchoring. I try to calm her as I call out, 'Breathe in and out through your mouth, Mrs March, try to let your body relax.'

'Relax yourself,' I tell myself as I fight with the blankets and her nightdress to get at her distended abdomen. At last I make it, and even through the copious layers of subcutaneous fat I can feel the uterus hard and risen beneath my hands. It relaxes at last, and Mrs March sinks back to the bed, her face red and sweating as she murmurs, 'I think that was a proper pain, don't you, nurse?'

Well it was certainly something, whether it was proper or not I am unsure, but I reply with assurance, 'Yes, I think that was a contraction, Mrs March, and I think that I had better examine you before another one arrives.'

But I don't have time; before I can prepare myself the next contraction arrives, less than two minutes after its predecessor. Now Mrs March and I fight with the mask of the gas and air machine, while Mrs White scrambles under the bed to retrieve the teacup.

12.25 p.m.

I have examined Mrs March and there is no doubt that her labour is well advanced. The cervix is dilated and the baby's head is pressing hard against it, she should be ready to have the baby within the next half hour. I write down the findings, making note of the fact that the uterine contractions were not discerned by Mrs March until labour was well advanced. But now they are discerned, and even after some help with a little pethidine the ceiling above the bed is working hard to stay in place as Mrs March cries out with each contraction. The sun has just come onto the bedroom window and Mrs March is a large lady; she has become very hot.

Mrs White is standing with just her head poking round the bedroom door. I call, 'Could you open the window please, Mrs White, and could you please make sure that the kettle is full and that it is boiling?'

I pay her no attention, I just hear the window open as I listen to the baby's heartbeat through the large and sweating abdomen.

Mrs March is ready to push. She has become very hot in the last hour. I am also very hot and I must put on a delivery gown over my uniform dress; this will make me even hotter. I make the decision to remove my uniform, and I put on just the delivery gown. With all tapes firmly fastened down its back I return to the bedroom, gowned and ready for work. I hear a man's voice as I enter the room and a short, thick-set man dressed in overalls is standing with his back to me. I make the assumption that this is Mr March as I speak, 'Hello, Mr March, I don't think that we are going to be too long now.'

He turns and looks at me for some moments. I am laying the delivery bag out onto a small table which once stood under the window, and which I have now placed in the corner of the room, and I hear the strong Midland accent as he asks, 'Yo the midwife then? Yo's an improvement on the other one. Her looked a bit old, is her finished?'

Before I have time to reply, Mrs March shouts out, pulls her legs up to her chin and starts to push.

I continue to assume that this man must be Mr March.

2.30 p.m.

The baby's head has just started to show; this is going to be a long and very hot process. I have discovered that the man is indeed Mr March who is in the bedroom with us, and I have managed to convince him that he should take the afternoon off work and that he should stay to help and support his wife. He has called out of the bedroom window, 'Joe, will yo tell the gaffer that the missus is havin' the nipper, and I'm stopping home with her.'

There is a reply, which I could not hear, and ensuing laughter, which I did not want to enquire about.

He returns to the bedside and I ask him to wipe his wife's face with a cool cloth. He looks around helplessly as Mrs White passes over a flannel which I had seen in the bathroom when I changed out of my uniform. He takes it from Mrs White and just touches his wife's forehead with it as he asks, 'So where's your mother? I thought her were going to be here when you had the babby.'

His wife has no time to reply as the next contraction arrives.

3.30 p.m.

The head is descending, but its progress is slow, I have encouraged her in English and now try in French as I call to her, 'Come on, *poussez, poussez,* Mrs March.'

But Mrs March is becoming exhausted. Her pushing is rather erratic, and instead of putting all her effort into pushing down at each contraction, she lets go of her thighs, and lifts the lower part of her substantially sized legs into the air. In order to control the baby's head I have had to lean across her leg, and now, as the contraction rises, she lifts me off my feet. As the contraction subsides and my feet hit the floor, I call out to Mr March.

'Mr March would you please come and hold me down or I'm afraid that if your wife lifts me again I might end up in the bed.'

I had smiled across at him as I had spoken, but now as his cold hands slide under the gown and around my waist I no longer smile. As the next contraction starts and his wife's leg rises, I hear him whisper behind me, 'Is that tight enough nurse, or should I hold you somewhere else?'

I cannot move, the baby's head is low, and I must concentrate on controlling its descent. The contraction subsides, I turn, and with Mr March standing only inches from me with his hands around my waist, I realise my mistake; the uniform is essential. Shaking myself free, I say, 'Thank you, Mr March, I can manage now.'

He looks at me, leering as he smiles, and I see Mrs White's sharp eyes glinting behind her glasses.

3.45 p.m.

Mrs March has slid down the bed, and Mrs White has pushed pillows in behind her. Now Mrs March is halfway down the bed, I can deliver the baby more easily if I kneel on the end of it. One more contraction and the head will be here. I press my knee down on the bed, and take my other foot off the floor in order to take control of the delivery. The cracking sound seems to last for a very long time as the corner of the bed lowers itself rather gracefully. At least that it how it feels, but Mrs March's large and imposing form descends at some speed, in less than elegant fashion, towards me. I, however, am not standing still waiting for it. With hands thrown out sideways I slide backwards. Something hard hits me across the middle of my back, the wind is knocked out of me, and I am thrown forward again. I can find nothing to grasp hold of, and I can feel myself sitting down again on nothing. The pain drags across the back of my now bare legs as they hit the window ledge. These old houses have sash windows, and being short and unable to reach the top of the window, Mrs White had pulled the lower half of the window up. I realise that I have come to rest with that part of my anatomy that few, with the exception of my mother, have seen, hanging out of the window over the pavement. Men's voices dominate my conscious as I struggle to pull myself upright, then I realise that below me men are heading towards the factories, the afternoon shift is going back to work. It takes only a millisecond for a crowd of men to gather and the cat calls and whistles ring out. But Mrs March's voice rings even louder as she shouts out and pushes.

As I struggle, I feel a hand not pulling at my arm, but to the delight of his assembled mates, the hand slides across my buttocks, and I am pushed forward. The laughter and whistling now fill the air; there will be much to talk about at the 'local' tonight.

Mrs March has come to rest on the mattress whose corner is now wedged against the wall under the window. Lowering my feet to the floor, and brushing off Mr March's hand, I drop to my knees and guide out the baby's head.

Mrs March calls out as if nothing untoward had happened, 'Is it born nurse? Is it born?'

I call out from my prone position as I reach upward to get cotton wool to wipe the baby's face. 'No, not quite Mrs March, just one more push.'

As I glance up I see Mr March standing at his wife's side and I note that the street has gone silent.

4.00 p.m.

The little girl, well I can't really call her little, she looks more like a three-month-old baby, lies across her mother's now not quite so distended abdomen, and gives vent to her feelings. There is no doubting the quality of her lungs.

Mrs March sits up, she is now halfway down the bed and one of her feet almost touches the window ledge as she sits forward and looks at her baby.

'Oh it's a girl, we've got a little girl.'

Mr March leans over his wife and pecks her on the cheek; she almost ignores him as she calls out, 'Look mother, we've got a little girl.'

A woman, whose body fills the doorway, glowers across at me. A little boy shakes free from her hand and runs towards his mother. Mr March scoops him up before he reaches the bed and I see the resemblance between father and son. But there is no doubting who his sister resembles – she is standing in the doorway, and pushing the man aside she kisses her daughter's forehead, and watches while I separate the child from her mother. I wrap the baby in a dressing towel and pass her towards her mother, but it is not her mother who takes her, it is her grandmother's hands that encase her. Kissing the baby's forehead the aptly named Mrs Bloom holds the child out at arms length, looks her in the face, and then passes her over to her mother. She looks around the room. Mr March disappears as he mumbles something about getting tea but a loud voice halts him.

'What's happened here then?'

Mrs Bloom squeezes past me as I head towards the dressing table to update the notes. Mr March starts to speak, but his mother-in-law stops him.

'I can see what has happened. I told you to get a decent bed for your wife to sleep on while she was carrying your child. But no, it's down the pub and across the road to the horses for you, you good for nothing.'

The afterbirth is delivered with no problem, and as I take the baby into the bathroom to bath her I suggest that, for the present, it might be more comfortable for Mrs March if something were placed under the broken leg to support the bed.

4.30 p.m.

The baby weighs in at ten pounds, six ounces, and as I take her back to her mother, suitably dressed in nightdress and pink hand-knitted matinee coat, I have to admit that she completes the trio. Mrs March smiles up at her mother and the three identical faces look at each other. The little boy sits on the bed by his mother and his baby sister lies on her other arm. Mr March is just putting the finishing touches to a pile of bricks which now replace the bed leg. Mr March winks at me, and whispers into the back of my head as he squeezes past me, 'If you are coming every time, I think we'll probably have six more, nurse.'

He kisses his wife's forehead, and says, 'I'll go down to the pub here and wet the baby's head, my love.'

He looks up at his mother-in-law and says, 'Bye, Mother, sorry you missed the show, it was pretty good.'

She looks after him with a malevolent stare. I hear the laughter ringing out from the pavement below. The story will, no doubt, be good for a fair few free pints; after all it had all the makings of a good French farce.

6.30 p.m.

The Case Book lies open on the kitchen table, the section designated for the recording of case number twelve now has a name in it, and I am assured that I will at least be able to enter for the examination; passing it is another matter. I transfer the details, which are at present in my notebook. It has been, for all intents and purposes, a normal delivery. No need to mention my position when the head was being delivered. The descent was rather slow for a second child, but as both mother and infant were rather weighty this is easily explained. I hear the steps sound on the stairs and, gathering up all my papers, I head down to the clinical room to report on the proceedings – well most of them, anyway.

23

Friday 27th April

5.30 a.m.

The phone rings, I am on my feet with the phone in my hand before Mrs O'Reilly gets up the stairs. She blows through her lips as she speaks.

'You don't have to do any more deliveries now that you have your twelve cases.'

I look at her for a moment and am just ready to give her the details, which I have just taken, when the thought hits home; I am no longer a midwife working from this address, I no longer have the right to say 'Pupil Midwife Compton speaking.' With a feeling of dejection, I murmur, 'It was Mr Alan.'

She requires no more and, turning, she starts to descend the stairs. It is hard to believe that it is all over. It has been the most exciting thing that I have ever done, the first time that I have been able to take responsibility for my own work, I can't believe that it has ended. Falling down the stairs behind her I get into the clinical room before her; she has gone to dress. I knock on her door, she does not reply but comes out dressed after a minute. She does not speak to me and I follow her into the clinical room as I say, 'Would it be possible for me to do this delivery?'

She looks at me over her glasses as she lifts a delivery bag. I mumble on, 'I know that I have got twelve cases, but some of them have been, well not quite normal.'

She stands with the bag in her hand and looks at me. I continue, 'Well it might be a good idea to have another, hopefully normal delivery, just in case they won't accept one of those in my book.'

Pushing the delivery bag at me she squeezes past as she says, 'You could have had this bright idea last night, and then I wouldn't have bothered getting up this early.'

6.00 a.m.

Fresh morning air hits my face as I whirl down the hill.

Mrs Alan delivers quite normally and pretty quickly, no complications.

10.00 p.m.

Mrs Pompolroy, who is one week overdue, delivers at 10.00 p.m. that night, again without problem.

24

Tuesday 1st May

2.30 p.m.

Only two pupils do not have the requisite number of cases, they both have twelve deliveries, but the post-natal care will not be completed in time. I sit with my head high, Mrs March, bless her, will be completed just in time.

Miss Bland stands before us, silver chain in hand and glasses on her nose. She rustles a sheath of papers as she speaks.

'I have the papers for your entrance to the Final Examination.'

She looks up at us expectantly. We sit stiff and upright, and stare back at her. What else is there to do, faint?

She gives a little cough and continues, 'This morning I want you to take your Case Book to your tutor, and if she is satisfied that it will be suitably completed by May 6th then I want you to each sign your Examination Entrance paper. If these papers are not signed and countersigned by your tutor, you will not be allowed entrance to the examination. Please take care of your Case Books, and bring them in to your tutor next week. Those of you who have already completed your books please keep them with you, and bring them in next week, when all the Case Books will be collected.'

She offers a benevolent smile to the 'goody two shoes' that are ahead of time and a giggly murmur goes around the room. She lifts her papers, reviews them, and continues speaking, 'I also want to remind you all that the practical part of your Community Midwifery Course will end on May 6th. On that date you will vacate your accommodation with your District Midwife, and you will return to the Old Nurses Home here at the hospital, where you will remain until the date of your examination on May 22nd.'

We receive a series of instructions on how to bring in our completed Case Books next week, and how to make sure that our tutor receives them in good time. I have little idea what else I would do with it if I didn't bring it into the School.

A buzz of conversation goes around the room at the departure of the tutors. Maureen is sitting at the other side of the room looking rather glum, and I can but assume that her friend has gone to her new job and has left Maureen to her own devices.

3.45 p.m.

The coffee shop in the student union building is crowded, in fact they have opened the double doors, and a few people are sitting outside in the sunshine. Quite a crowd sits around two tables which have been pushed together in the corner. They are all sitting with their heads down, and the tables seem to be piled high with books. I see a face rise out of the mob, but Tony does not look at me, with fingers up to his mouth he stares ahead, and then biting his lip he lowers his head and disappears once more into the melee. Finals are upon them. It is to be the last time that I see Tony, and I never find out how the tennis match went, or how he did in his finals.

I climb off the bus at my usual stop, I am feeling bright and chirpy, the final case has been accepted, and my exam papers are signed. I stand on the pavement as the bus drives off, and it hits me that this will be the last time I return from the hospital to Mrs O'Reilly's flat. I had become accustomed to being here; I had almost forgotten that it would end. I climb the stairs, all is quiet. Is Mrs O'Reilly out? Has someone else gone into labour? Then I notice that the door to the clinical room is partly open so, throwing my bag onto my bed, I run back downstairs and into the room. Mrs O'Reilly stands with her back to the door, and her hands are deep in the drawer containing the case notes. She appears not to have heard me, and I call out as I cross the room, 'Hello, has someone gone into labour?'

She does not turn as she speaks, but continues with her work.

'No, not to my knowledge they haven't.'

I stand behind her uncertain as to what I should say or do now, but she fills in the space, and again without turning addresses me.

'I've got to make sure that all these notes are completed properly before you go. You might have your book completed for your exam, but these notes are legal documents, and should I ever need to go to court with one of the cases that you completed, I will be totally dependent on these notes. I alone will stand there, you will not be called.'

I stand behind her, silent. That she should doubt me comes as a shock, and it hurts. I had thought that she had trusted me, but now I see that I am just another student, just another 'ship in the night' that passes through. I find my voice, 'I hope that they are all right, I completed them as I went along.'

246

'Hmm,' she says, her voice disappearing into the drawer.

I linger – should I offer to help or should I leave her to it? Again she reads my mind as she speaks.

'You'd better go and put the kettle on or we won't be getting any tea today.'

With relief I race up the flight of stairs, I was starting to feel emotional about this parting but now I realise that my success as a midwife in Mrs O'Reilly eyes is as important, and probably more important, than the examination will be. The kettle boils, its whistle sounds the call to refreshment, and I hear Mrs O'Reilly's footsteps on the stairs, slower than mine, but surer.

We drink tea in comparative silence only the odd query is made, and replied to.

'Case Book accepted?'

'Yes, yes, no problems foreseen, and I have signed up for my exam on May 22nd.'

The tea and biscuits are finished as she rises.

'There are one or two things that I would like to raise with you.'

I follow her down the stairs, my heart beats loudly. Some notes and the Drug Book lie on the small white table in the middle of the room. She walks over to them as she starts to speak.

'When you delivered Mrs Burns, you gave pethidine?'

I try to interrupt her.

'Yes, I wrote it up in the Drug Book.'

Raising her hand she stops me.

'I am not questioning that, what I see in the notes is the time when the drug was given, but I see no accompanying date.'

I look hard at the notes, and then back to the Drug Book, but I do not speak. Looking into my face she continues.

'When I have to account for the drug, I will have no date for the drug being given in any notes.'

She hands me a pen and, with scarlet cheeks, I fill in the date at the appropriate place.

The time difference of the birth of the Macaronis twins is not made clear. She almost smiles as she comments, 'Thrones have been lost based on such record keeping.' She stands back while I rustle through the notes, and with cheeks still burning with shame and resentment at being called to task, I amend them as necessary.

Mrs O'Reilly carries on. 'I see that we have two sets of notes for Mrs Bloom, according to one set she has been delivered, but according to the other nothing has yet happened.'

I start to explain, but again I don't get very far. Mrs O'Reilly continues, 'I know what happened; you fell asleep in the bath. But which set of notes do you want to remain on file? And would you please remove and dispose of the spare set before Mrs Bloom has another baby, and before life, for me, becomes confusing.'

The mistakes pile up. The notes for the lady with the mynah bird are still on file. It would seem that she did not belong to us after all; she lived just beyond Mrs Quinn's area. Mrs O'Reilly had been notified that she had been admitted to hospital with some weird viral infection; I wonder if it had come from the bird.

7.00 p.m.

The file is closed and so is the door to the clinical room. I hope that neither have been closed onto any of my mistakes. Mrs Stone speaks as she climbs the stairs towards us, 'Do you want a few chips putting on? I'm doing some for him.'

We sit in front of plates of chips, sausage and egg, and a large plate of bread has been buttered while the kettle was boiling. We both dig in, and Mrs O'Reilly smiles for the first time since I got home.

'So what did those tutors have to say today?'

I regale her with today's lecture, and her good humour is fully returned. I mumble into my teacup, 'I am sorry about all those mistakes.'

She stretches her mouth sideways, and nods as she puts her cup down.

'Don't worry, that's what you are here for isn't it? If you knew all there was to know, there would be no need to come here, now would there? Mind you I've had some who thought that they knew it all, thought they knew more than me anyway. By the way I'll take any deliveries that come up until you finish.'

I start to protest but she stops me.

'It's nothing to do with you, it's just the way the course runs, you now have a week to finish your cases and to check up on the notes of the ones that are already complete.'

With a sigh of sufficiency she pushes back her plate, and rises to pour the tea.

25

Tuesday 8th May

7.30 a.m.

I open my eyes, the window is not bright and the crucifix lies in dull grey light. I have never talked with Mrs O'Reilly about religion and I have no idea if she is Catholic. I have noticed no other symbols of religion in the flat, but she had told me that I could be called for church on Sundays, should I wish to be. As I have long ago given up on religion I declined to take up the offer.

Then I remember Mary and the Convent, and decide that she must have some relationship with the Catholic Church. Mary has gone home to Ireland with Naomi, her uncle had taken them last Thursday. The Mother Superior had rung Mrs O'Reilly to inform her, and Mrs O'Reilly had told me; I had felt as though I had been put in my place.

Dr Wainwright had rung to say that Mrs Wood had responded well to treatment, and that she would soon be home. He had passed Mrs Wood's thanks to Mrs O'Reilly and my part in events seemed to have been forgotten. Suddenly I feel life to be sad and all my past work incomplete and ineffectual.

On my last visit to the Wallers' house Mr Waller had been at home. He had been back to work but he had been sacked for hitting one of his fellow workers over the head with a spanner. I felt that I should have helped Mr Waller, and not have left him to his own devices. I do hope that he will soon get another job, and my eyes fill as I think of that inoffensive young man who only wanted to do his best.

The Macaronis twins are both doing well, but I don't think I can say the same for their two grandmothers. However Mrs Macaronis is out and about. A car drew up at the house on Saturday morning, and flowers and a bottle of wine were delivered to Mrs O'Reilly. The wine has not been opened and I don't think that I will be invited to drink any of it.

Baby Copperopolis had attended a premature baby clinic at the General Hospital. He had not been admitted to hospital, but it had taken some time to get him feeding. And to think that one day he'll be as big as his father!

I smile when I think of Mr Clarke and feel a little more cheerful, I don't know what had shaken him up, maybe it was the thought of losing his wife, but on my last visit he had opened the door to me, and I hardly recognised him. He had left the house almost as soon as I got there, and Mrs Clarke, with pride pouring out of every pore in her body, had told me that he had an interview for a job.

I have not spoken to my friend the mynah bird again, and I had intended to try and find out if all went well for Mrs Ramshaw and her baby, but I had not found the time to do this yet. I had seen Mrs West out with the baby only yesterday, she was still talking 'forty to the dozen' and I had to work hard to escape her, but I have to admit that she has a fine son.

7.45 a.m.

I hear the rattle of cups; Mrs O'Reilly must be in the kitchen. I had heard the phone ring at five thirty this morning, and I was out of bed and with the phone in my hand before my brain had started to work. She had taken the details from me, and without even a 'good morning' she was gone, and today I must be gone. For a moment I lie, unsure of how I feel. Half of me is pleased that I have been successful in completing this most exacting part of the course, and proud that I have not fallen by the wayside. Two students have found it too much for them, and have removed themselves from the course, two more will find out today if they can be entered for the examination. I hear the kettle whistle, and I know that I must say goodbye and go. No time for emotion or sentiment, as Mrs O'Reilly has said, this is the real world. I came for a specific reason and I have completed it. Now it is time to move on.

26

Tuesday 22nd May

2.00 p.m.

The square is bright with warm May sunshine, it is also alive with the electricity of human tension. Two weeks have passed at enormous speed, little daylight has been seen on the journey between classroom and library, only the written word, either in a book or on a blackboard seems to have passed through to my brain. But now I sit in Tavistock Square, and the hot London sun shines down on my dark blue hat and dress as I wait for the brown doors, which lie at the top of a flight of stone stairs, to open and admit me to the examination hall. Eighteen pupils from my course arrived by train this morning, and now we sit, or stand, huddled together at the corner of a small ornate garden whose low stone wall gives seating to those of us who no longer find it possible to stand. There must be many courses coming to their fruition this afternoon as the square is scattered with young people who frantically seek the last modicum of information from book or notes and who, with dark-ringed eyes, constantly glance up at the door. I have not seen Tony during my stay at the hospital, he is also taking finals now and I glance around the square in case he should be there, but I cannot see him.

Voices sound and the square comes to life; the door has been opened. Hastily pushing the book, which I have not even glanced at, into my large canvas shoulder-bag I fall in step behind another blue uniform. Mrs O'Reilly had shaken my hand, and she had even kissed me on the cheek as she spoke.

'You'll be all right, just keep cool and think on your feet, you've done that very well while you've been here, so I have no doubt that you will pass the viva with flying colours.'

I see her face now as I climb the stone steps and enter the dark hallway. It takes minutes for my eyes to adjust to the dull light and we concertina up into a tight knot as the first group of people to enter come face to face with a line of small tables, each of which is manned by a suitably serious guardian. Having found our table we stand in line, I hold my Examination Entrance cards before me as if it were a crucifix warding off Satan. But Satan appears in the form of a long, grey face which, devoid of any colour or emotion, beckons me towards it. Having taken my card with a thin, grey hand, the face looks down at it, looks across at a list on the small table and, in a voice which is directed over my shoulder, says, 'Table number twenty three.'

The long dark cloakroom with its smell of clothes and polish reminds me of school and as we file into it, almost heel to toe, I am sure that I am back in the second form at Stonemore Grammar School. A hand gives me a ticket, and a voice speaks to no one in particular.

'Hang your coat and bag on this peg number; you may take nothing into the Examination Hall.'

I hear someone behind me speak, and the voice says,

'Yes, you may take a handkerchief with you, but nothing else.'

Frantically I search for a handkerchief. Mother would have been ashamed of me if I didn't have one; I don't have one. I see blue hats moving away, and I hurry to join them. The small corridor outside the cloakroom opens into a wide hall whose high ceiling makes it look enormous. There is little light at ground level; that coming in from windows, high in the walls, finds it difficult to descend, as, on both sides, the walls are partitioned off by unpainted wood, which rises eight or ten feet from the floor. Leather-topped tables, lit by table lamps, stand at intervals along the centre of the hall, each faces towards one of the wood partitioned sides, and at each sit two people who, in avid conversation, ignore all passers by. I pass through a second hall and then, in the dim light, my number – twenty three – comes into vision.

2.30 p.m.

I can hear my heart pounding. It sounds so loud I am sure that I won't be able to hear anything that is said to me. I raise my eyes; a leather-topped table lies before me, and on it, along with an array of papers, lies my Case Book. Behind the table, and with her hand on my book, sits a woman who wears the same uniform as that worn by our senior tutor. At a small table which stands next to the desk sits a man. He wears a grey suit, which looks as though it has seen much service, a white shirt whose collar lies a little off centre, and a tie of quite resplendent colours. A voice speaks, and I am recalled to order.

'Miss Compton, is it? Please do sit.'

I have not been able to assure them that I am Miss Compton, but I sit. No introductions are made on their part and we get straight down to business. The Case Book has been opened and I assume, from the number of papers sticking out of the book, that there are many points that need to be qualified.

2.45 p.m.

I walk towards a partition, which has number twenty three stapled to its wooden surface, and towards which both my inquisitors face. The cubicle is enclosed only on three sides, not the top, and the fourth side, through which light enters readily is an opaque, leaded window which was obviously designed to allow light to enter the large hall but whose effort is now trapped in this small enclosure. A single bed takes up most of the space in the cubicle, and on this bed lies a woman. A small table stands beside the bed, and on this table there lies a set of antenatal notes, or should I say a set of antenatal forms. It is my responsibility to complete them and turn them into notes. All goes well at the beginning, the name and address are pencilled out and the section for previous pregnancies presents few problems. Half an hour is allocated for this examination and for the completion of the relevant parts of the notes. I can hear Maureen's voice and then I realise that she must be in the adjoining cubicle. I hear Maureen ask, 'So, in what year was your third child born?'

There is a long silence, and then a loud voice speaks, 'I think that would be nineteen forty-three, nurse, I know it was the year that our dad broke his leg. No wait a minute I lie, that was the year I had our George, when me dad broke his leg, I had Margie the year before that. It is Margie you want to know about isn't it, nurse?'

The answer has nothing to do with me, but I smile to myself as I remember Mrs Clarke and, turning back to my patient, I continue on with a smug smile on my face as I ask the next question.

'When did you have your last period?'

She smiles at me sweetly as she replies, 'November the seventh last year. I remember it started just after bonfire night.'

I cut in quickly just in case she wants to reminisce as fully as the lady next door is still doing.

'Was that a normal period?'

'Oh yes, nurse,' she replies.

I smile back at her, and suggest to her that she is at present six and half to seven months pregnant, and that her expected date of delivery should be somewhere at the beginning of July. She nods and replies, 'Yes, nurse.'

This is too easy, I think to myself. I can still hear Maureen fighting it out over who did what in the previous generations. I feel the top of the uterus, and listen with the foetal stethoscope. I make the diagnosis that the lady is about seven months pregnant. Putting down all the implements, I ask my last question with complete confidence.

'Has anything unusual happened to you during this pregnancy?'

I feel the smile on my face fade as she replies, 'Well I had a miscarriage three months ago, nurse.'

I look at her for some moments before I speak, the smile on my face now rather forced.

'Now are you sure that it was a proper miscarriage? I mean you could have lost quite a lot of blood without losing the baby.'

She stops me in full flight.

'Oh yes, nurse, it was a proper one, I went into hospital and I had one of those operations, the doctor said that I had lost the baby.'

In panic I look at the notes again, a classic pregnancy. I feel the uterus again, it is at the right height, the baby is of normal size for a seven-month pregnancy, and the heart sounds loud and clear, no chance of a multiple pregnancy. A bell rings and I hear a loudspeaker voice call out.

'Will you please complete your notes, you have five minutes remaining.'

What more can I ask? What more can I do? All I can do is to record my findings, without further investigations and information I can write down nothing other than that which I have found by question and external examination. I thank the woman for allowing me to examine her, and wish her every success with her future delivery. The bell sounds and I leave the cubicle.

3.15 p.m.

I sit by the table the notes in front of me. I have explained my findings, and without blinking an eye have said that the woman had stated that she had undergone a termination of pregnancy in January of this year when she would have been three months pregnant. We discuss the possibility of the woman having been mistaken about the procedure which she had undergone, the possibility of there being twins, one of which survived, and I had ruled out the possibility of there being a multiple pregnancy at present. The man leans on one elbow and looks me in the eye, his yellow tie, bright with small flowers, shows below his hand.

'Supposing I was to tell you that the woman did undergo a dilatation and curettage on the date she stated, and that all foetal matter was removed, what do you say then?'

For a moment I look at my notes, and then I speak almost to the table.

'She could have a bicuspid uterus; she could have had a foetus in each side of the uterus.'

I hear him moving his papers and look up at him. The sharp blue eyes are still on me, and they seem to be challenging me. The challenge is accepted, and I blurt out, 'Or maybe someone doesn't know how to do a D and C, maybe someone should take some lessons before they do another one.'

Now the smile breaks, and his voice laughs as he replies, 'She is my patient, so I will take heed, and I will pass your message on to my senior registrar the next time I see him.'

The bell goes, and in a flurry of activity I am on my way out of the hall. People I know are behind me; someone touches my arm and speaks.

'Do you know who that was at your table?'

'You mean the chap in the flowery tie?'

'Yes,' she replies. 'It was *the* Mr Clarke, you know, the obstetrician who wrote our main obstetrics book.'

27

Thursday 24th May

I sit at home reading a book, my bother Jack comes in.

'How did the exam go?' he asks.

I moan and pull a face.

'As good as that, eh? I don't know why you bother, you could get a job down at the doctor's surgery, he is looking for a receptionist. If you took that you could relax a bit, stop at home, you might even find a bloke around here willing to take you on, there might be someone daft enough. When do you get your results anyway?'

I reply without looking up from the book.

'Next month, but I think that I've blown it. And I don't think I'd want anyone from around here to take me on, whatever "take me on" means.'

Father enters the room so the conversation ends. I know my father's opinion, I don't want his tirade again.

28

Saturday 26th May

Rompton seems cold and empty. It had always felt cold to me when I was a child. The wind constantly blows across the hills from Crich. The last hill of the Pennine chain, from which you can see across four counties, is a windy place, a place which I had visited many times with my father. Riding up and down its hilly terrain I was sure had given me the backbone which my father still finds so hard to deal with.

The market had always managed to lift my spirits when I was a child. It had been the place where I had learnt how to face the world alone. Fighting for the family's rations when mother was too ill to leave the house has made me self-sufficient and determined. Shopping with mother when she was well, searching the stalls for a bargain, and visiting the café for mother's favourite – a cup of coffee. These had been the greatest delights of my childhood. However, not today. Today I feel flat, I see few prospects ahead of me. Mother has gone into a shop to buy a pork pie for father's tea, and I stand alone. A voice calls my name; I cannot be sure from which direction the call comes. I shade my eyes from the sunlight as Alan Bunting walks towards me.

29

Friday 22nd June

8.30 a.m.

Birds quarrel in the eves of the house as I lie listening to them. This silent country life is making me quite lethargic and everything is an effort. I hear my mother's voice calling and for a moment I ignore it, then I realise what she is saying, 'There is something come in the post for you.'

Now I am heading down the stairs, bare feet on carpet and pyjama legs flying. A large brown envelope lies on the kitchen table, I look at it almost mesmerised. The words 'Central Midwives' Board' are emblazoned across its top. Mother turns, 'Well open it then, you can't read it until you do.'

I pick it up and turn it over in my hands. Mother passes me a knife and, taking a big breath, I slice open the envelope. A sheet of white paper slides out, and I see the words '. . . having passed the First and Second Examinations of the Central Midwives Board . . .'

Other words follow, but I see no more. I have passed.

4.30 p.m.

I stand in the phone box in the village and dial Alan's number. Mother had been overjoyed, the neighbours were called in and gallons of tea were consumed. My brother Bob had returned home from work and I had promised to go for a drink with him. A female voice answers the phone, I don't understand a word she says I just ask, 'Is Alan Bunting there please?'

Voices shout loud in the distance and after what seems an age Alan speaks to me. Preliminary congratulation over he asks, 'Are you coming back down here then?' I need no time to contemplate as I have already received application forms for a post in one of Burlington's midwifery units.

7.30 p.m.

I walk with my father on this fine June evening. We know that daylight will last for several hours, so our planned walk, which we have done many times before, takes us unto the hills and across the Derwent Valley.

9.45 p.m.

We stand looking down into the gathering dusk. The sky over the distant hills is still golden. I smell tobacco and know why we have stopped. Having tapped his pipe on the heel of his shoe, father fills the bowl from a leather pouch and I wait. He speaks after the flare of the match has shown me his still strong face.

'Are you going to marry this bloke, the one that you are so busy chasing after?'

Smoke billows across to me and the perfume, which reminds me so much of my childhood, almost makes me cry. In my childhood his man directed so much of my future, but now I direct my own, and almost with laughter in my voice I reply, 'I shouldn't think so, Dad. Anyway, he hasn't asked me as far as I can remember.'

His voices comes through a long expulsion of smoke, 'I suppose tha'd better bugger off then and earn thy own living at whatever trade tha's good at.'